38 BAHADURABAD

ZEEBA SADIQ

38 Bahadurabad

faber and faber
LONDON · BOSTON

First published in 1996
by Faber and Faber Limited
3 Queen Square, London WC1N 3AU

Phototypeset by Intype London Ltd
Printed in England by Clays Ltd, St Ives plc

A CIP catalogue record for this book is available from the British Library

ISBN 0-571-17793-X

2 4 6 8 10 9 7 5 3 1

for Araminta and Nicholas

They volleyed Lee Chong back and forth, and their memories built virtues that would have surprised him, and cleverness and beauty too. While one told a fine tale of that mercantile Chinaman the other waited impatiently to top the story. Out of their memories emerged a being scarcely human, a dragon of goodness and an angel of guile. In such a way are the gods created.

Sweet Thursday, John Steinbeck

Prologue

I played with knives for that first three months, though I bear no scars. I did, however, try an overdose, a morbid precociousness for a nine-year-old. I suppose it must have been in the spirit of medical theory therefore – my mother enjoyed a vicarious apothecarial celebrity among her friends – that she took me along to my father's surgery. Whatever the reason, it worked, for when I climbed those four stone steps at 352 Frere Road and stumbled through the heavy double doors, the janitor-boy bidding ostentatious salaams, I was suitably chastened.

It was the first time I had been there since his death and the silence chilled me. There was already a smell of musty neglect and, oddly, patches of damp had formed on the walls, though it hadn't rained for some weeks. I noticed that the medicine cabinet was bare – the vultures had been already, though goodness knows where they had found a key. That apart, it was exactly as my father had left it when he last stepped into the street and closed the door behind him, and it occurred to me then that this was the first time in my life I had entered that room without him.

My mother made straight for his desk. I followed her instinctively, wiping away tears with the sleeve of the white qamiz I had worn every day since his death. It had been one of his last gifts to me. I watched her as she pulled a key from her handbag, slipped it into the lock of one of the drawers, and eased it open. There was little in her expression to indicate what she was doing.

I stood beside her, clinging to the arm of her qamiz,

and peered into the drawer. There were three photographs lying there, that was all. I recognised two of them immediately: the first of myself, my sixth-birthday photograph, pulling peevishly at my father's trouser-leg as he struggled to hold his smile for the camera; the second of my mother leading in Dum-Dam after his victory in the Karachi Derby.

The third I had never seen before. It was a faded sepia picture of a tall handsome woman, two young boys by her side. The woman wore a distinctive hat, which I imagined to be a light blue or green; the two boys were squeezed into school uniforms that seemed too small for them. All three had fair skin.

'Who are these people?' I snapped at my mother. 'Why are they here?'

My mother appeared to notice me for the first time, and taking the photograph from the drawer took my hand and led me to the grey leather examining-couch beneath the shuttered window. We sat together and she allowed me a closer look at the picture. I stared hard, and in the shorter of the two boys seemed to recognise something.

'One day, Zeeba, you might meet these boys,' my mother explained, 'but you must always remember that it was you that your father loved most.'

Dr Sadiq and the Servants

The day my father first made tea for the servants it is reported that my mother suffered apoplexy. The servants didn't drink it, fearing it to be a test of their obedience. My poor father! What need had he of servants?

Dr Sadiq rose at six, slipped into his immaculately ironed shalwar kurta, crept through the sleeping house, and out on to the marble-tiled patio. He lit his first cigarette and, as was his custom, surveyed the quarter-acre of garden before him. He noted that the bougainvillaeas were looking particularly fine this morning, but that the geraniums required some attention. The lawn, too, needed some work. He arranged a schedule of work in his mind, stubbed out the cigarette in the beautifully crafted glass ashtray, a gift from old colleagues at Guy's Hospital in London, and then set to work. Dr Sadiq savoured this first hour of the day, alone in the garden while the city slept. He was short and slight, and glided easily between the strange farrago of plants and trees that he had assembled during his five years in Karachi. Drooping coconut palms hung over the rose-bushes, the banana tree by the rhododendrons. Two fir trees stood in the centre of the garden, with mangoes, pomegranates, and pears lining the perimeter wall. Only the south-eastern corner lay bare where the paan plant had grown. He had removed it the previous week, a grudging concession to his wife who had claimed quite irrationally that it would attract snakes. But he had plans for that corner. Rakshanda, his stepdaughter, was visiting from Scotland, and she had thoughtfully brought him a mixture of packet seeds. The stones for a rockery had already been ordered.

The doctor attended his work without fuss, and by seven had trimmed the rose-bushes, clipped the geraniums, and turned the soil. As the sun came up the garden became swamped in an exotic cocktail of fragrances: jasmine, mogra, mango, and banana, all mixed into a sweet tropical blend. Occasionally he would pause to enjoy the early-morning birdsong: the sparrows chirping insignificantly around the lawn, a blackbird singing proudly from his tree-top vantage, and the crows squawking greedily around the refuse in a neighbouring garden. But their song was soon lost amid a crescendo of street noise and activity, and the doctor continued with his work. By eight he had watered the plants, mowed the lawn to a quarter-inch, and returned the tools to their respective hooks and cupboards in the small wooden shed at the rear of the house. He lit his second cigarette and relaxed in the wicker chair in the shade of the patio. At a quarter past eight the gardener arrived, and at twenty past Mrs Sadiq turned restlessly in her bed and heard the two of them talking outside. There was a time when she would have stormed into the garden and screamed imprecations at the doctor. Mrs Sadiq had never lived in England and so was at a loss to understand the strange habits of behaviour that her husband had imported from that country. A doctor cured illness, and a gardener tended plants and trees – the two were mutually exclusive to Mrs Sadiq. Social convention would not allow her to release the gardener, however. If you can afford a garden then you must have a gardener was her simple, if not extravagant philosophy. But now she suffered her husband's eccentricity in silence. The gardener too had given up protesting. He was a conscientious man and it was always something of an embarrassment to him to accept his wages. So now, simply to please the lady of the house, he contented himself pottering around the garden without purpose.

The city was awake by 8.30 when the cleaner and the washerwoman arrived, and they joined the gardener in the kitchen to be served tea by the doctor. They had overcome their earlier suspicions and now enjoyed the enigma of the master of the house waiting on them. And they did concede that he made wonderful tea. Even his mother-in-law had begun to join them on occasions. But not Mrs Sadiq. For her it was one indignity too far. Only when she heard her husband taking his customary cold shower did she rise. Shemsunessa Shirazi loved her husband dearly, but she could never have imagined on that fateful day five years earlier that the handsome doctor from England whom she was to marry would come to display all the proclivities of a servant, and not those of a respected physician. If only he would let the cleaner polish his shoes, though, and allow the gardener to help him with the lawn, she thought. He was sixty now, and hadn't his own doctor warned him long ago of a dangerous heart condition? No cigarettes, no strenuous work, just two shots of whisky a day and definitely no sex, he had said.

And so it was on this particular morning that he entered the dining-room with his young daughter in his arms, Baby Zeebande, four years old, a gift of his disobedience. Dressed impeccably in shirt, suit and dickie-bow, he bade his wife good morning, put the child down, and settled into his breakfast of hard-boiled egg and buttered toast, chatting amiably to his wife as he ate. He remarked on the weather, and told her of his plans for a rockery. He had also received word that the car had been repaired and was ready for collection from the garage. But Mrs Sadiq was not in a good humour. She had caught sight of the cigarette stubs in the ashtray outside and was now struggling to keep her counsel.

And when the doctor announced that he would be taking a lift home with his friend Yahya that evening, she finally erupted. She could tolerate most of her husband's wayward friends, but not Yahya. She despised Yahya. He was loud, he was excessive, and he drank. Mrs Sadiq had drunk alcohol only once, a large gin and orange at a wedding reception, and afterwards she had seen the moon in the toilet. Yahya was, in fact, a generous bon viveur who had stoked the lady's ire only when he had had a bar installed in his brand-new car. And so it was that whenever he called on the doctor at his surgery with the offer of a lift home, though his car was much newer and faster than the doctor's own, the journey invariably took twice the time. And when the doctor would eventually arrive home and step clumsily from the car, Mrs Sadiq was never in any doubt that the moon had been in the car. See if I care if you go to an early grave! But who will support your daughter then? Who will pay for her medicine when she's ill? Who will buy her school books? Where will she find new shoes and clothes? Will your friend Yahya support us when you're gone?

A car-horn sounded in the driveway. The doctor's taxi had arrived. He kissed his daughter goodbye, smiled meekly at his wife, and for the second time that morning crept from the house. The car reversed carefully into the street, the large iron gates closed behind it, and the gardener hid among the bushes as he heard the menacing sound of Mrs Sadiq emerging on to the patio.

Nani's Story

Mohamed Ali Shirazi lies deep beneath the waves, some thirty miles off the coast of Sind in the shark-infested waters of the Arabian Sea. My grandmother told me this today. Sitting on the balcony of our apartment, looking out beyond the Clifton Beach, she had said calmly, and without emotion, 'Your grandfather's out there.'

'Always on ships, always at sea,' she had continued. 'From Iraq to the rich land of Hind, from Bombay to the land where old ladies wear make-up and sell newspapers, and then from London all the way back again, always at sea. The last time I saw his face it was being wrapped in a tablecloth by the ship's crew.

'He was a good man, your grandfather, though I never learned to love him. He was forty-three when we married, and I was just sixteen, still a child. He was very educated, and always treated me with kindness and consideration. Our families had known each other for several generations, and though his parents had moved from Shiraz to Basra towards the end of the last century, he was still proud to be a Persian. When he was twenty-two he had travelled from Basra to Bombay to seek his fortune. He could speak the language of the Arabs, the Turks, and the Persians, as well as English, and he soon prospered there. By the time I married him he had his own catering company, supplying food to McKenzie & McKenzie, the biggest shipping company in India. But despite his wealth he had simple tastes, and it was as a consequence of this that he was forced to divorce his first wife. By all accounts she was a nymphomaniac who made constant demands on him. "How can I work if you want sex all the time?" he was heard to say to her. "My customers won't come to my bed to sign contracts." '

'She was only demanding her conjugal rights, Nani,' I teased my grandmother. 'Don't be such an old fogey.'

'Tooba, tooba,' she scolded me. 'Respectable girls don't say such things, Zeeba. The poor man was too tired to work. What choice had he but to divorce her? How many children did she want?'

I pursued my grandmother. I loved to embarrass her.

'How did you conceive Appai, then? Immaculate conception?'

She reddened immediately.

'You've lived too long in England, Zeeba. You never used to speak like that.'

I urged her to continue.

'Well, when I fell pregnant, my husband decided that he wanted his child to be born in the place of his own birth. He was desperate for a son, and imagined that it would be auspicious for us to return to Iraq. I told him that I didn't want to travel all the way to Basra in my condition, but he was quite adamant. He could be very stubborn, and I eventually yielded to his will. He left his business in the hands of a trusted friend, and we set sail from Bombay. But the journey was not to be as auspicious as he had imagined, and though I left Bombay a pregnant wife, I returned there a pregnant widow.

'We had been at sea some time when we called at the port of Karachi. I hadn't eaten well on the journey and, as soon as we docked, he rushed straight into the city to arrange for the best food to be brought to my cabin. Would you believe that he even paid for waiters to come and serve me on the ship? Karachi was an expanding city, and there were many fine Persian restaurants there. To this day I still remember what we ate – chicken kebabs, biriani, roast leg of lamb, and a basket of fruit for dessert.

'We must have been about forty minutes out of Karachi when we finished our meal. "That was the finest meal that I have ever had," my husband said, a split second before his face crashed into the empty plate before him. My husband was stone dead, and those were to be the last words that I ever heard him speak. "That was the finest meal that I have ever had."

'Ship's regulations forbade us returning to port, and so he was wrapped in the tablecloth on which we had just dined and placed in an empty cabin. There was no facility for keeping his body on board ship until we arrived at Basra, so the following morning, before sunrise, shortly before prayers, he was hurled to the fishes, and I did not leave my cabin again until the ship returned to Bombay several weeks later. As his body slipped into the water I bade him farewell, and promised him that I would bring his son up to be a good man, just like himself, and that I would never let him forget the father that he had lost at sea. The child for whom he had paid so dearly was born a month after I returned to Bombay. The son for whom he had died was born an eight-pound girl: your mother.'

The Yuccas

Mrs Sadiq was furious, and her husband was entirely to blame. Who had ever heard of such a thing, growing trees indoors? The trees were two fully grown yuccas that Mrs Sadiq had bought from the wife of a European diplomat who had just completed his tour of duty in Pakistan. They had come in huge brass pots engraved with crests and she had paid a considerable amount of money for them. It satisfied her sense of station that plants that had once adorned a Western embassy should now stand outside her own house, as befitted the home of a doctor. And so she had placed them either side of the wrought-iron gates to the driveway for all the street to see, careful not to obscure her husband's name-plate screwed to the gate-post: DR S. M. SADIQ, MBBS, MRCPS, LRCS, FRCS. No other house in the street could boast such fine specimens and her husband was delighted when his old Ford Consul rattled up the street after morning surgery. He wondered if at last he had persuaded his wife of the contentment to be found in the cultivation of plants, and looked forward to introducing her to the mysteries of his garden. However, he would need to advise her that the polluted scorched atmosphere of a Karachi August was perhaps unsuitable for yuccas, and that house plants had different requirements from the garden shrubbery.

'I suppose they grow trees in the house in England, do they?' she had snapped, hurt by his apparent ingratitude. He hadn't meant it that way of course, and had assured her that there would be no question of drilling a hole in the ceiling as the plants grew.

'They will look nice in the lounge, Chundi Begum,' he had encouraged her. 'Just by the windows. They will get enough sun there. Squirt a little water on the leaves each day and water the compost once a week and you'll soon discover that you've got green fingers.'

And so, reluctantly, with the help of Sultan, she had unseated the plants from their perch by the gate-posts and carried them down the driveway, struggling round the parked car and up the patio steps, and into the lounge. But so as not to allow her husband too much kudos in the event of his advice proving sound she had placed them against the south-facing wall of the lounge, either side of the burgundy chaise-longue that graced the length of the room.

Zeebande didn't like to use her parents' bathroom because she was frightened of the frogs. She wished her father would seal the door to the plumbing under the bath. She couldn't use her grandmother's bathroom because the discarded matchsticks left by the card players made her nauseous, and her brother and sister always locked their rooms. Needs must, however, and the lounge was the quietest place in the house during the afternoons. Climbing on to one or the other of the new brass pots that her mother had recently placed by the wall she balanced on the rim and sent a steady trickle down into the soil below, her backside resting on the stem of the plant. There were no frogs or matchsticks in the lounge.

It was just under four weeks later that the doctor passed his wife in the hallway struggling with a huge plant pot in her hands, the yucca visibly unwell, the leaves hanging sadly like the broken wings of a bird.

'Trees do not live in houses,' she berated him. 'They belong outside. I am taking them back to the gates.'

'You will kill them,' the doctor warned her a few minutes later when he found her emptying a gallon of water into the compost.

'We shall see,' she retorted.

Mrs Sadiq's yuccas died within three days of their banishment to the gate-posts outside, and so ended the lady's flirtation with the world of flora. The ornamental brass pots were returned to the sitting room, now empty of their charges. Needs must, however!

Mrs Malik was drunk that evening when she stumbled over the brass pot during a card game. Breaking her fall, her hand squelched into the liquid that gushed from the pot on to the carpet.

'It's piss!' she cried, catching the stale stench as she picked herself up from the floor.

Zeebande caught her breath as the flattened palm of her mother's hand thudded into her cheek.

'If you want to behave like a Hindi, then go and live with a Hindi,' Mrs Sadiq seethed.

'But I hate frogs,' the child screamed as she went running from the room.

Appai's Story

My mother drank ink the day she rejected Sheikh's proposal. The taste was unpleasant and it made her ill. But love or no love, her children were part of the package. No children, no marriage!

'Why did you divorce Wajahat Mirza if he was so rich and famous?' I asked my mother.

Half an hour later I wished I hadn't bothered. I was just passing the time of day. My mother was in garrulous tenor, however.

'It was Mehdi who was our undoing,' she said. 'Mirza was a philanderer and a bad husband, but if I could have got him away from his brother, got him out of Bombay, then Rakshanda and Faridoon might have had a father. But he wouldn't hear a word against Mehdi, and so eventually I had to leave. I was living in a madhouse.

'When I first met Mirza I was an innocent seventeen-year-old. *Mother India* had just been released and he was the talk of the Bombay film world. I was at a showbiz party with some friends when he caught my eye from across the room. Though he was much older than me I couldn't keep my eyes off him. He had so much charisma and presence, and when he approached me and asked me my name I thought that he was the most charming man I had ever met. People had always told me that I was an attractive child and so when he told me that I had the perfect features to be an actress and that he would make me a star I had no hesitation in believing him. I was completely star-struck. He spoke to me all night at the party and the following evening he took me to one of Bombay's finest restaurants. I was bewitched by him, and when he stripped me of my virginity later that night I was powerless to resist. We were married two months later. Your grandmother did everything in her means to dissuade me, but I wasn't for turning. I was going to be a film-star, and Mirza and I would be the perfect tinsel-town couple.

There was disappointment in my mother's voice, still resentful that she had been so easily taken in.

'Did you ever audition for the films?' I asked her.

'No. I was too busy protecting my children from the lunatic in my husband's house. When I married Mirza it seems that I also married his family.

'He was one of four brothers. Only one, Asghar, lived away. The others, Mehdi and Murtaza, lived with Mirza and depended on him for a living. They leeched off him until his dying day, and even as I speak one or other of them is living in the apartment in Bombay that rightfully belongs to your brother and sister as his heirs. I swear no one in that family has done a day's work in their lives apart from Mirza. God knows how they're going to feed themselves now that he's dead.'

Mirza had died the previous week and ironically had spent his last days in Karachi close to Appai. I was surprised that my mother could sound so bitter about something that had happened so long ago.

'What should have been the best years of my life were ruined by that family. I was young, beautiful, and from a prosperous Persian family. The world was my oyster. If only Mirza had been more severe with his brother. It would have been no loss to this world if he had pushed Mehdi from the balcony of the fourth-storey apartment where we lived.

'It was Zara who first warned me of Mehdi. Zara was the wife of Murtaza, the youngest of the brothers. Being the youngest he was Mirza's favourite and Mehdi used to get furious with jealousy. It is said that on one occasion he had mixed a poison into Murtaza's drink, but that Mirza had walked unexpectedly into the kitchen and had picked the glass up himself. With a flourish of arms and an exaggerated stumble Mehdi had managed to knock the glass from his brother's hand. But it was such a melodramatic performance that Murtaza and Zara were immediately suspicious. They found the poison later, hidden in the kitchen, and it was because of this incident that Zara warned me of Mehdi, advising me to be especially careful with Farid, for now that Mirza had a son of his own it was inevitable that Mehdi would lose his position in the affections of his brother, and it was equally inevitable that he would try to do Farid some harm. By this time, of course, my dreams of stardom had been shattered and so my children became my whole world, my only reason for living.'

'Don't be so bloody dramatic, Appai,' I chastised my mother.

'It's true, Zeeba. You can't imagine what it was like in that house. I lived in permanent fear for my children. It's no exaggeration. Every single day I had to be wary of Mehdi's voodoo and black magic. Shall I tell you what he used to do? Each full moon he would walk naked to a nearby cemetery and pray to Satan. He would stay there all night, and the next morning when he returned home, he would slit the throat of a chicken and splash its blood all over the roof of the building where we lived. He also had an irrational hatred of Hindus, and at the Hindu festival of Diwali he would go to the Hindu crematorium and pick hair and bones from among the ashes and then throw them from our balcony at the Hindus as they celebrated in the street below. But the strangest thing that I recall was the episode when I was breastfeeding Rakshanda one time. I was sitting on my favourite chair, the one closest to the main door of the apartment. I remember that Mirza was strangely agitated about something that day and that he wanted to consult Mehdi about some matter. He sent the boy-servant, Abdullah, to call him from his room. Abdullah was a timid superstitious creature who was terrified of Mehdi. He knocked lightly on the bedroom door. "Tell my brother that I shall be ten minutes," he told the boy when he answered. A half-hour later he still hadn't appeared and Abdullah was sent to call him again. "I shan't be a moment," he called from his room. When he still didn't appear I could see that my husband was beginning to get angry. He was busy with his writing and so as not to disturb him I went to fetch Mehdi myself. Though his antics worried me because of my children I certainly knew him for the parasite that he was, and so I had no compunction about walking straight into his room and telling him that he was keeping his brother waiting. He was lying on his bed, staring at the ceiling. He didn't look at me when I spoke. "My husband wishes to speak to you," I told him. "He called you an hour ago." I left the room, not waiting for an answer. A chill of fear ran down my spine when ten minutes later he appeared through the main door of the flat, and not from his bedroom. I swear to you that I had been sitting by the door for two hours and that no one had left during that time. There was no other door and it would have been impossible for anyone to leave without me knowing. Besides, I had seen him lying on his bed just ten minutes earlier. He flashed me a wicked grin as he came through the door and walked to his room. "I've been to the shops," he remarked casually as he walked past me. Abdullah was trembling with fear.'

'Are you making all this up?' I interrupted my mother.

'I swear to God, Zeeba, it happened exactly as I have told you. The man had the devil in him. You know, at night-time we used to hear the strangest noises coming from his room, of knives being sharpened, and what sounded like vegetables being sliced. I was used to his bizarre behaviour by that time and would have thought nothing of it, but what was strange was that the sound rang crystal-clear throughout the house, as though it was being amplified by loudspeakers. I could never find an explanation for it, nor for any other of the bizarre happenings. And there's another thing you'll find hard to believe. In all the time that I lived in that house I never saw Mehdi's wife. I didn't even know her name. All that I knew of her was that she had been engaged to be married to Mirza at the time that he met me and proposed. Having been passed over by Mirza she was handed down to Mehdi, the second brother. She was never allowed out of her room and she used to have to defecate in an old ghee tin which was emptied each day. On the rare occasions that she did leave the room with Mehdi she was covered from head to foot in black cloth. We couldn't even see her eyes. Mehdi would lead her straight from their room and out of the apartment. She wasn't allowed to utter a single word to us as we were considered to be evil beings by her husband. It infuriated me so much that Mirza put up with this nonsense, for though he was the eldest brother he was completely in Mehdi's grip. Mehdi was forever giving him voodoo potions to drink. I think that at first he drank them just to humour his brother, but there was certainly some strange ingredient in those cocktails as Mirza became ever so docile and subdued whenever he drank them. When I first married him he was a stern, self-confident man, but now he allowed Mehdi to do as he liked. And there was nothing anyone else could do. Asghar and Murtaza could see what was going on but could do nothing. Mirza was the only breadwinner in the family and so if he was prepared to tolerate Mehdi's behaviour, so were they.'

'No wonder you're mad,' I teased Appai.

'Maybe so,' she conceded, 'but I wasn't mad then. I wasn't going to let that lunatic brother ruin my life. I was at the end of my tether, so I decided to move to Pakistan. Your grandmother was living in Karachi by that time with her third husband, Mohsin. You know the one. That dreadful bore who still visits from time to time. The one who thinks that he's an English gentleman.'

Appai never minced her words.

'I had visited Pakistan on three occasions and on the fourth, when I told my mother of Mehdi's black magic, she begged me to stay. I didn't need much persuasion. But Farid and Rakshanda still needed a father and so my mother sent Mirza a ticket to come and join us. He stayed for a short while before returning to Bombay. I received a letter from him a few weeks later saying that if I wished him to live in Karachi I would have to accept his brother too. That was unthinkable. The reason that I had left India was to escape his brother. I therefore wrote back saying that if he preferred the company of a lunatic to that of his wife and children then he was welcome to it. I told him that I wanted a divorce and that I would forgo any financial settlement if he renounced any claim to his children. He agreed by return of post. And that's why your brother hates his father so much, the ease with which he just discarded his children.

'Well, in any case, we moved in with Nani and Mohsin but things didn't work out. Mohsin was a lot younger than your grandmother and had only married her for her money and her respectable position in society. And behind all that unctuous bonhomie he was really a nasty piece of work. He hadn't counted on two young children in the house and for some reason he particularly hated Farid. When I found out one day that he had tied Farid to the bed and whipped him with his trouser-belt I decided to move out. No gold-digging gigolo was going to lay a finger on my children.

'I managed to rent a small house and moved in with your brother, sister, and Laxmi. I needed some income, of course, and so bought a cow and started selling fresh milk to the neighbours. I know it's hard to imagine that now in the centre of Karachi, but then it didn't seem so strange. Your grandmother offered us support of course, but I wanted to be independent. It was my own responsibility to feed my children. So I worked hard with Laxmi's help and things began to get a little better. I converted half my kitchen into a little store where I used to sell spices to the neighbours. We also prepared meals for local workers. Laxmi and I used to cook right through the night and then deliver the meals during the day. We never seemed to sleep, but we were happy enough. We cherished our independence, our insularity. We existed only for each other.

'Sheikh was a military man, a friend of my stepfather's. He was a good-looking Punjabi and I fell completely in love with him. It was the first time that I had experienced real love. After we first met he began to visit me regularly and eventually popped the question. But unfortunately there was one caveat. He didn't want the responsibility of my children. I couldn't believe the dilemma I found myself in. The one man that I had ever loved was asking me to give up the thing that I held dearest, my children. I couldn't conceive of them being put back in the care of that beast Mohsin, so I refused his proposal. It broke my heart to do it and in a moment of despair I drank a bottle of ink. I don't know why. It wasn't going to help my children. I just felt that my whole world had come to an end. But the ink did nothing but make me ill for a while and gradually I tried to live again, vowing to devote my life to my children.'

I had never heard Appai speak like this before, and

for the first time I understood why I sometimes felt like an outsider in my own family, never having shared those difficult times with my brother and sister.

'Around that time my mother decided to divorce Mohsin. He had embarrassed her once too often, flirting with younger girls at parties. So she decided to move in with me and the children. But our small house wasn't really large enough for us all so we rented a larger place in Bahadurabad. By coincidence our new place was in the same street as a renowned doctor, a doctor that I had met many years earlier at my husband's house in Bombay. They were old friends from Lucknow. When Rakshanda fell ill it made sense therefore to take her to see him. He remembered me, of course, and so I invited him to the house for dinner one day. Though he was much older than me we found that we shared a lot of interests. We both loved the horses and gambling, and he was also a keen cricket fan, so we started meeting regularly. Sometimes he would come round for one of our card games, and other times he would take me to the races. Some months later he proposed marriage. I hesitated at first, but eventually accepted, for though I had no shortage of suitors at the time, it was his fondness for my children that made him the ideal choice. Besides, he had two grown-up children of his own and didn't want to start another family. And I certainly didn't want any more children.'

'Thanks very much, Appai!' I interjected.

'Well, do you blame me! Your brother and sister never asked me to talk into tape-recorders at three o'clock in the morning.'

'You're the one who wanted to talk,' I reminded her.

'Will you two go to sleep, please,' my grandmother called from her room.

'Ignore her,' my mother said. 'Did I ever tell you about . . .'

'Let's go to bed, Appai. It's late.'

'You're as bad as your grandmother. Only three o'clock in the morning and you want to go to bed . . .'

The Diagnosis (1)

They were all agreed. They had never seen such a thing before. The doctor, his wife, her mother, the maid, and even the cook, all peered down in wonder and fear at the bright purple specimen. In all his years as a physician Dr Sadiq had never seen its like. It had always been a matter of some pride to him, his unrivalled reputation as a brilliant diagnostician, but the purple stool sitting in the centre of the toilet basin had him perplexed. Certainly his daughter looked well enough, but her multi-coloured bowel movements were not the symptoms of a normal healthy child.

The doctor had suspected haemorrhoids the first day when his mother-in-law alerted him to the scarlet stains on the toilet bowl. But a thorough check-up had revealed nothing untoward in his daughter, and enquiries of her school had satisfied him that the food had not been to blame. When the child proudly pointed at the mustard-coloured specimen the next day, however, he put her straight to bed and took samples to his surgery for analysis. The results had offered him some reassurance, but this third day's offering had him beside himself with anguish. He now ushered the audience from the bathroom, assuring them that all would be well and that he knew just the medicine that was needed. He then determined to seek the advice of colleagues. He knew of an excellent scatologist in London: a telephone call would surely yield dividends.

Young Zeebande veritably purred with contentment in her bedroom, wallowing in the love showered on her by her mother. Mrs Sadiq had sat with her daughter for a whole hour after the fuss had subsided, promising her a picnic at Kiljee Lake as soon as she had recovered, and feeding her with her favourite sweet paans. The young child was only too well aware that she had been an accidental and unwelcome addition to her mother's progeny, and that she could never compete with the marble-skinned, hazel-eyed beauty of her elder sister Rakshanda or the silent moody charisma of her elder brother Faridoon. But now she was centre-stage where she belonged, firing her coprolitic rainbow at the toilet basin.

For a week Dr Sadiq had poured over his dusty medical manuals, and Mrs Shirazi had beseeched Allah's intervention. Mrs Sadiq had sought the assistance of a respected local dervish whose piety was known to have cured a child's stutter, and the cook had taken to personally testing each dish before allowing it out of the kitchen. Each of them slept now, as the afternoon heat reached its peak. Laxmi rested on the lounge floor, her head balanced on a strong leathery hand. The door slightly ajar, she was able to see down the hallway, cautious of any intruders. She started as a door creaked open, but relaxed when she saw her young charge entering the bathroom opposite. Knowing that the child was unwell she waited to see her return to her room. Zeebande duly emerged, but instead of returning to her bedroom toddled purposefully towards the adjacent storecupboard. Laxmi, her curiosity triggered, edged closer to the door and saw the child return with a tin box in her hands.

Zeebande had often seen her sister shuffling in and out of the bathroom with tiny white pillows in her hand. She had also noticed the tiny spots of red on her sister's underwear when she had sat with Laxmi at the washtub. It had certainly not escaped her notice that it was at the time of the pillows that her mother showed most concern for Rakshanda. Spurred on by her first day's success therefore, she had been encouraged and emboldened to make her way, one by one, through her tin box. And now she stood on the seventh with a tube of green oil-paint in her hand. Squeezing it down into the basin she splashed on a little water for effect, and then depositing the empty tube through the small wooden door that accessed the plumbing to the sturdy bathtub, she was careful to wash the paint from her hand before running to call her grandmother to see her new emerald masterpiece.

'See what you have done? You have driven the whole house mad with your nonsense!'

Zeebande froze as Laxmi proudly held the paint-tube aloft. Her grandmother nearly passed out with relief.

'Red!' Laxmi proclaimed, retrieving another tube from beneath the bathtub.

'Mustard!'

'Purple!'

'Yellow!'

'Blue!'

'To every question there is an answer,' Dr Sadiq told the first-year medical students at the Seventh Day Hospital where he was occasionally invited to lecture. 'There is only one time that I have truly been unable to find a diagnosis. My daughter was five years old at the time . . .'

Laxmi's Story

'He pricked me with a needle on our wedding night.'

Laxmi had massaged my mother's feet as we each recalled our Suhag-night. She had listened patiently to our uneventful tales, so very privileged, so very middle-class. And then her words stabbed at me as I caught the stench of cooking mutton from a neighbour's kitchen. Mutton had not been eaten in our house since that day, many years earlier, when I had spat the foul flesh across the dining-room table and vomited. My grandmother had crudely disguised the meat in a vegetable sauce, convinced, or so she claimed, that I would develop the scales of a fish if I continued to gorge on the treasures of the Mouths of the Indus.

Laxmi spoke again. I wanted her to stop, but she was many years away now.

'All night . . . all night . . .'

Her words thundered around my head. The night was still and the city seemed to listen. She hesitated, her face betraying the horror of her memories. The anticipation was suffocating. My grandmother had occasionally alluded to Laxmi's past, but I had always been spared the details. I didn't really want to hear, but it was like a festering sore – though I knew that it would hurt I wanted to touch it.

'He was a madman, Zeeba. A sadist. It was my wedding night and I was alone with a stranger for the first time in my life, and it was my kismet for that stranger to be the devil himself. We were in a small room at the back of my mother's house. He stood in the far corner leering at me. The white-washed walls were stained yellow from cigarette smoke, the only furniture was a chest of drawers that sat just below the iron-rod window, and a single naked bulb hung from the centre of the ceiling. I lay naked on the mattress, terrified, too frightened to move. I didn't know what was going to happen to me. How could I? I was too young to know.

'My husband seemed to be searching for something in the drawers. He took out a needle and moved towards me. It was an old sewing needle, brown and rusty. Tears welled up in my eyes, but I forced myself not to cry. He crouched down beside the mattress, grinning, his eyes full of evil. He pointed the needle at me and then began to stab. All over my naked body. My legs, my arms, my feet. Even my buttocks. Everywhere. That brown rusty needle puncturing my skin. It seemed to go on for ever. Just stabbing, stabbing, stabbing. It hurt so much, but I was too frightened to cry. I just lay there, numb, my young body covered in bruises. I tried to think what I had done wrong, why I was being punished.'

The evening call to prayer disturbed her from her thoughts. She looked up, her eyes glazed with pain.

'Why did you marry him, Laxmi?' I asked. My question sounded crass, but she smiled kindly. She had expected it.

'There wasn't a choice, Zeeba. There was never a choice. From the day I was born it was my kismet to marry that man. I was shackled by hundreds of years of tradition, hundreds of years of duty. Duty to my parents, duty to my brother, duty to my sisters. A duty to feed them when they were hungry, to provide for them when they were in need. A duty to put their well-being before my own happiness. And after all, it was a simple equation, Zeeba. My family wanted food, my husband's family wanted me, and so a deal was struck and I was sold. Yes, put bluntly, I was sold. Sold for sixty rupees.

Dear God, Zeeba, is that all that I was worth? Just sixty rupees?'

Poor Laxmi. What had they done to her? I could see a lifetime of pain in her eyes. I took her hand.

'You know, Zeeba, things were very different then.'

I smiled. That was how she always used to start her stories when I was a child.

'The first time that I ever saw my husband was when my mother led me to the altar on my wedding day. I was too young to know what was really happening, but I remember feeling dizzy, so many people around me, such unusual smells, and the pandit chanting strange music. And then I saw him, my future husband, sitting beneath the canopy, garlanded in roses. He seemed so old, as old as my father, and I remember noticing how the whites of his eyes were yellowing and his teeth were reddened from betel juice. As my mother urged me forward I felt as though I was being led to the gallows. Allah, they might as well have done. I died that day in any case . . .

'We had been such a happy family. We lived in a small shanty home in the slums near Bombay Central Station and were very poor. But that never mattered. We kept our house clean and my parents worked hard to bring us up as best they could. There were seven of us altogether. My parents, of course, my brother Ananda, and my three sisters, Pahlee, Sahoo, and Sonie. Sonie was the youngest and my favourite. We were inseparable. I used to look after her every day while my parents were working. We would get up together early each morning when my mother woke for work, usually at about four o'clock. My mother did several jobs to bring in money, cooking and cleaning for other families. Each morning I would pick Sonie up and we would follow my mother to work. We would always stop at our favourite bread-and-tea stall where she would buy us breakfast. I never wanted to leave and would make excuses, saying that I was afraid of the dark. But each day she would stroke my hair and tell me that I had to look after little Sonie and that I should take her home. Later in the morning I would prop Sonie on my hip and we would take my father his lunch at the Cola factory where he worked. I loved my father and when he could afford it he would treat us to a cold fizzy drink. It was such a happy childhood, roaming around the neighbourhood and talking to all the people that I met. But then everything changed. Sixty rupees changed my life.'

Laxmi had smiled as she spoke of her family. But a dark shadow crossed her face as she once again recalled her marriage.

'That morning, the morning after my shadi, I lay on the mattress, paralysed with shock. I had lost all track of time, but I could see the light of dawn through the window. And then I remembered that my father had said the night before that he would collect me in the morning. My mother-in-law had reluctantly agreed to me visiting my family the next day as I had screamed and shrieked when they tried to drag me away with my husband. I didn't want him to see the state that I was in so I washed and dressed quickly, doing my best to hide the bruises. I rushed to greet him when he arrived. I was so happy. I thought my nightmare was over. But of course it had only just begun. I didn't even get to speak to him. My mother-in-law sent him away, as she was to do over the days, weeks, and months that followed. Each time that he called he would beg them to allow me to see my mother and sisters. He told them that little Sonie had cried every day since I had left.

' "Just for a few hours, Begum," he would beg my mother-in-law. I was so homesick and I cried every time that he came around. I would cling to him and implore him to take me home. But it was useless. He was poor and powerless. He hadn't even been able to afford a dowry for my wedding. He would reluctantly free himself from my grip and then walk away, his head bowed, dejected. I was truly alone, abandoned to an endless purgatory of beatings and housework. I was worked like a mule and only given leftovers to eat. There were four of us in the house. Parassan my husband, my wicked mother-in-law, and my husband's sister. There wasn't an ounce of kindness in any of them. From dawn until dusk they just worked me to the bone. After only a week of marriage my husband had kicked me from the mattress. I was left to sleep on a matted rug on the floor with just my arms and elbow for a pillow. I had only a thin sheet to cover me, no matter how cold the weather.

'It was around this time, four or five months after my marriage, that my husband returned home from work one day having been drinking with some of his cronies. I was in the kitchen cleaning. He suddenly grabbed me from behind and began to pummel me with his fists. No reason. I hadn't even spoken. Well, I must have had a flash of courage for I broke free from him and began to run. Out of the room, out of the house, and down the road towards the railway station. I knew my way as I had often had to collect water from a well near by. I don't know if he tried to follow me. I was too frightened to look. It was rush hour when I reached the station and I was swallowed up among hundreds of commuters. I began to cry, for I couldn't read and so didn't know which train to catch home. I had no money either. I hadn't seen a single paisa since the day I had married. Luckily a kind lady showed me the train and I was able to slip past the ticket-inspector among the crowds. I felt a surge of relief as the train pulled into Bombay Central. Familiar sights and sounds. I was home.

'My mother cried with joy when I walked into the house. She was alone in the kitchen, squatting over the chapati stove. My sisters and brother had been sent to the bazaar as they had been getting under her feet. My father was still at work. She was devastated by my appearance. I had been a happy healthy child, but now I was wan and emaciated. I gorged on the food that she gave me. I hadn't eaten a good meal since my shadi. It's funny. She asked me so many questions, but she never asked why I was alone, without my husband. She must have known what I had done, but she was just so happy to see me.

'I lay down beside her as the day began to take its toll on me. I watched her as she kneaded the dough for the bread. She seemed to have aged. A lifetime of toil showed in her face. I suddenly felt so sorry for her. That sixty rupees couldn't have lasted very long. I promised myself that now I was home I would do everything I could to make their lives a little easier, and with these thoughts I must have drifted to sleep.

' "What are you doing here?" my father bellowed. I awoke with a start, startled by his tone of voice. I thought he would have been glad to see me. My mother became hysterical as he trembled with rage.

' "The only time that a Hindu girl leaves her husband's home is in her funeral cloth," he screamed. My mother pleaded with him, but he wasn't listening. He grabbed me, marched me out of the house, and didn't let go of my arm until my mother-in-law opened the door to let me in. I needn't tell you what they did to me, Zeeba. I became a punch-bag for them all. But I was young and it wasn't easy for them to crush my spirit. I ran away several times, but now, not only was I getting beatings from my husband, but also from my father. I began to realise that my efforts were futile. There was no way out. It was my kismet.

'It was about this time that my husband's mother and sister began to take me along to work with them. They worked in a leather factory owned by an Englishman. For about a week I just watched them work. I hated it. The smell was terrible, but everyone used to be told that it was a special privilege to work there as people travelled from all over the world to buy the skins. I think it was used for musical instruments, especially tablas. After a week I began to work too, pulling the intestines from the carcasses of goats and cleaning the skin. It was terrible work, and in the evenings when I got home, my hands swollen and gashed, my mother-in-law would make me pound raw chillies with my bare hands for my husband's meal. Such pain, Zeeba. I used to hide in the toilet and cry.

'Men and women all worked together at the factory. We were all menial workers. A few months after I started there I began to notice a boy always staring at me. At first I was frightened. I was only young, and what could I know about love. Besides, my husband also worked at the factory and I didn't dare think what he would do. But it wasn't long before this boy started smuggling me little gifts. Sometimes he would send a samosa, and sometimes sweets. He would send them to my two girlfriends as they weren't married and so it was easier for him that way. But young as I was I knew that they were meant for me. In any case my friends used to tease me because they had also noticed him staring at me. After some time he began waiting at the factory gates when work had finished. I would cover my face with my sari out of embarrassment. This carried on for a long time, staring at me all day in the factory, the little gifts for lunch, and then waiting by the factory gates every evening. Though I was flattered, I began to get scared. There was a Hindu custom that if a married woman was seen with another man she would have her plait and nose cut off. Also, I couldn't bear the idea of my parents being thrown into jail.

'Anyway, the matter came to a head one day when I went to a friend's house for some tea after work. She was a nice old lady who worked with us. She was a Muslim from Allahabad and lived near the factory. Everybody liked her and she used to share her lunch with me and my friends, Kali and Sita. We called her Maosi. Live and let live, she always used to say.

'On this particular day I was alone at the factory as my husband and his family were at a wedding. I had to get home for the housework of course, but when Maosi asked me to walk home with her for some pakora and tea I was so happy to have the opportunity to take a break from my life of endless work. Even the smallest amount of kindness shown me made my life worth living. Anyway, I was at Maosi's house when all of a sudden Noor appeared in front of me. That was the boy's name, Noor. I was so surprised to see him. I hadn't known that he was related to Maosi. I covered my eyes.

' "Don't be shy," Maosi said to me. "Noor is a nice boy and looks after me. All people from Allahabad are nice," she teased. She pulled some clothes and jewellery from a drawer and handed them to me.

' "These are for you," she said. "Noor has been saving up and has bought them for you."

'I couldn't speak. I couldn't believe what was happening. And then Noor spoke. This was the first time that he had ever spoken to me during all those months. He asked me to go with him, to run away with him. He told me that he loved me and that he wanted to get me away from all the misery that I had suffered. I remember him saying that he had noticed my swollen hands covered in sores, and that he would look after me if I went with him. I was so shocked. I couldn't believe what he had said. I had to say no of course. I couldn't possibly go. I couldn't bring shame on my family. My in-laws were evil, cruel people and would have made life hell for them. I couldn't see them insulted and humiliated, so I refused. Allah, Zeeba, maybe if I had gone I might have found some happiness. But it wasn't to be. I went home and that was the end of that. Noor didn't arrive for work the next day and I never saw him again.

'Some months later my mother and father turned up at the house. They had decided to move to Poona and had come to bid me farewell. I was devastated. Poona was so far away. I clung to my mother and began to cry. I begged her to take me with them. I couldn't bear to be left alone to my beatings. Every day I was whipped. Two or three times, every day. They beat me with anything they could lay their hands on. My body ached and I just wanted to be with my mother. I needed her love. I had forgotten what it was to be loved, to have my hair stroked. All I knew was the pain of rods, of clothes hangers, of sticks. I whispered to my mother as I clung to her. I told her what they had done to me and implored her to take me away. But my father came into the room and told me to let go. I held tighter. She slipped a piece of paper into my hand. It was their new address. I threw it down. I didn't want it. I didn't need it. I was going with them. My mother must have had a flash of courage. My in-laws were occupied talking to my father. She took my hand and began to run. Out of the house and down the street. But then someone called and I knew that we had been seen. Some of my husband's friends chased after us and dragged us back to the house. I was beaten to the ground. My mother tried to stop them but they slapped her across the face. She fell too. They tripped my father as he went to help. My mother whimpered as they hurled abuse at them. I could feel the pain of their humiliation. Back in the house my husband whipped me until I passed out. When I came to I looked as though a train had hit me. I felt numb. Dead.

'Despite his humiliation my father returned the next

day. He pleaded with them to allow me to go with him for just a few hours, just to say goodbye to my brother and sisters. But it was useless. They were evil people. They had no morals, no mercy. Come back when she has mothered two children, they said. Then she can come with you. So he left, broken and humiliated. He never returned, and that was the last I ever saw of my family. I was completely alone, at the mercy of tyrants. I do remember a glimmer of hope though. A letter arrived one day. It was from my mother. My elder sister was getting married and my parents wanted me to travel to Poona for four days. I was cooking in the kitchen when the letter arrived. My husband brought it in and read it to me. He asked if I would like to go. I was elated. He must have seen it in my face. He grinned and came towards me. He handed the letter to me but just as I was about to take it he dropped it in the stove. I watched in disbelief as my one fleeting hope of happiness turned to ashes. That was the last letter I received. I hadn't even had the chance to see the address. But I swear, Zeeba, even at my age now, if I had that address I would go looking for them.

'After that my life became an endless misery. I was treated worse than a dog. I worked all day at the factory and then came home to cook and clean. My husband did nothing. He had given up his job at the factory and spent the day in front of the mirror, grooming himself. Everything had to be just right for him. Every day I had to clean and starch his shirts. I remember that one day he sent me to the bazaar to collect something. It would never occur to him to go himself, of course. When I got back he was waiting in the doorway.

' "Who have you been talking to?" he asked.

' "No one," I replied, astonished.

' "Don't lie," he screamed. He grabbed me, and then retraced every step that I had taken to the bazaar, asking all the sellers if they had seen me talking to anyone. I yelled at him. What could he do? He had taken everything that I had, everything that I loved. My parents were gone. He had stripped me of my dignity. I had nothing. He could beat me, sure enough, but he would do that anyway. He had never needed a reason for that. So what more could I lose? He dominated my life with a stick. He was completely irrational. I never knew what I would be subjected to from one day to the next. And then he made me give up my job at the leather factory. He must have seen that I had friends there. I got a job in a glass factory making bottles. But that only lasted a month. He made me give it up and got me a job at a coal factory. But not for long. He decided that I ought to work in someone's house. I suppose that that way he could make sure I would never meet any friends. I got a job in a nice household, cooking, cleaning, and doing odd jobs around the house. They were a pleasant couple and I remember that they had a daughter who was pregnant. I got paid each week but I never saw the money. My husband would take it off me straight away and spend it. After a while he began asking me to go and ask for more.

' "Go and ask your nice Sahib and Begum for a rise," he would mock. I had to refuse, of course, and so he would beat me up. One day he walked into the kitchen in a rage. I had just finished cooking and was cleaning the saucepans. He strode over and kicked me.

' "Give me some money," he screamed. I told him that I had none. He knew that I never had money. He had always taken it all. He grabbed me by my hair and pulled a carving knife from a drawer. He held it to my throat.

' "Get me some money, whore, or I'll kill you."

'I had had enough. I couldn't take any more. I had nothing to lose. I knew with certainty that if I came home without any money that night he would beat me to death. So I decided that this was the time to go.

' "All right, I'll go," I managed to say. "I'll go and ask them for money."

'He still wouldn't let go and he whipped me with a bamboo stick until I was out in the street. I was in a daze. I felt that I was going to faint. I walked and walked. I had suffered so much that I didn't care what happened to me any more. I had made up my mind. I was never going back. I walked away from him in my torn sari, bare-footed. My young life flashed before me. How I hated them! It wasn't so much what they had done to me but the way they had treated my parents, the way they had murdered my babies. How different my life might have been if I had had a child to love. But they were never given a chance to live. I remember the first time I fell pregnant I had gone to Paral Hospital for the Poor. Though I was young I wasn't stupid, and I knew that if I was to have a healthy baby then I would have to go to a big hospital and do as the doctors told me. They had taken blood samples and had told me that my baby would be fine, just so long as I took everything easy. But of course it didn't stand a chance. I was shown no mercy. Though I was weak and thin during my pregnancy I was made to work from morning until night. Sometimes I even had to work right through the night when the Muslims had their festivities, sweeping and cleaning, and washing the huge pots that they cooked the food in. Meanwhile the beatings never stopped. In fact during my pregnancy my husband refined his technique and began to kick me in the stomach if something displeased him. What chance did my babies have? My mother-in-law even refused to take me to the hospital when I went into labour. I screamed with agony but it made no difference. Three children I bore. The first lasted ten minutes, the second two, and the third was born dead. "Let her bear two children and then we will let her visit you." Those words to my father rang in my ears like a sick joke. I was so weak after my third pregnancy that I couldn't go to work for four or five days. But my husband still needed his money. I was still working at the leather factory at the time so he went to my superiors there and told them that I had died in childbirth. He told them that he needed money for my cremation. When my friends heard this they had a collection to buy flowers and a white shroud for the funeral. They all came round to my house after work. They turned white when they saw me. I couldn't understand why they had come, but when I saw the flowers and shroud it quickly made sense. Nothing that my husband did surprised me any more. But strangely enough I remained calm. I just smiled and suggested that as all the preparations had been made everyone should continue with the ceremony and burn me. After all, I had been dead for a long time now. My friends just stared in disbelief. They explained what my husband had done and said that they had all been so upset to hear of my death that they had had a collection for my flowers.

'After my first child died I was told by my mother-in-law that I was unworthy to touch food and so I was fed on a diet of dried bread and black coffee. What did I care, though? It seemed that ever since my wedding day I had just been waiting to die. I was a walking corpse. All I remember was constant hunger, the blisters on my feet because they wouldn't allow me to wear slippers, and the daily routine of washing and drying my one and only sari. But looking back at that time my biggest grief is that I never got to hold any of my babies. They barely had a chance to move before they were dead. Fatima, my next-door neighbour, had fallen pregnant at the same time. We always wanted them to be born together. She had a lovely baby daughter. I had a still-birth.'

Laxmi took a sip of water from the beaker by her side. The evening was hot and sticky.

'Where did you go when you ran away?' I asked her.

'I went to the nice Begum's house. I don't know how I got there. I just found myself there after hours of walking the streets. When the Begum answered the door she was horrified at the state that I was in. I begged her to hide me, to show me some mercy. She let me in.

'That first night at my employer's house I didn't sleep very well. I could only think of all that I had suffered and how I was, hopefully, safe now. In the morning the Begum explained to me that now that their daughter was pregnant she would be finding her own home with her husband. She explained there was therefore no real need for my services any more. But she promised that her daughter would need someone once the child was born. I begged them to let me stay until then. I told her that I would rather throw myself in front of a train than go back to my husband. She said that she would discuss it with her husband in the evening. It was later that morning that my mother-in-law arrived at the house. I was on the roof pounding spices but I could hear her voice. She began wailing. But they were crocodile tears, Zeeba. She asked the Begum if she had seen her beloved daughter. She said that she had been searching the city all morning.

' "Please help me find my precious daughter," she wailed. But the Begum must have taken pity on me. She denied having seen me and the evil woman left. It was very kind of them to give me shelter for a few days and to lie for me. But in the end they lied to me too. After a week they gave me fifty rupees and took me to stay with relatives of theirs. They said that I would be safer there and that they would call for me once their grandchild was born. I was very grateful and looked forward to going to work for their daughter. They were a good Christian family.

'I was taken to a place called Kalinagar. They were a big family with twelve children. I had to work hard, cooking for fourteen people, cleaning, scrubbing the floors, and twice each day walking two miles to the nearest well to fetch water in two big gourds, one balanced on my head and the other tied round my waist. But at least I had a future to look forward to. Little did I know that it was the beginning of a new nightmare. After just two weeks they told me that I had to leave. They told me that they had heard that my husband was looking for me and that they did not want to be arrested by the police for harbouring me. They told me that I must leave straight away. But it was night-time and I begged them to let me stay until the morning. They said that I wasn't their concern and they just threw me out into the street. They didn't even pay me for the two weeks' work I had done. I was so scared. It was dark and I didn't know my way around. It was the middle of the night so I just sat outside their house in the street. What else could I do? I couldn't sleep for the noise of the squealing pigs in the local farms. It was such a frightening noise. I wanted to pray but didn't know who to pray to.

'When it started to get light I picked myself up and walked to the nearest watering tap. I washed and then wrapped my shredded sari around me. Some kind people gave me directions to the train station. I sneaked on to a train to Paral where my Begum and Sahib lived. But it was further disappointment when I got there. Their daughter had already left. She had never had any intention of taking me with her. And the Sahib explained that he couldn't afford to offer me work any more. But I suppose he was a kind man deep down. He took me to the house of a friend of his. He was a retired schoolmaster living in Nak Para near J J Hospital. But once again I was made to beg. He said that he couldn't afford to pay me wages. I told him that I didn't care, just so long as he gave me a crust of bread to eat and a corner to sleep in. So he took me on. There were four of them in all. The husband and wife, and two children, a daughter and a son. Time passed on and it seemed as though I had been there for an eternity. But it was in fact only two months, two months of endless drudge. Cooking, cleaning, scrubbing floors, washing clothes. I was never paid. I wasn't happy there but that didn't matter. I had never been happy since the day I was told that I was to marry.

'It was after two months that I woke one morning with a terrible headache. My whole body was aching. I couldn't move. I thought if I lay there for just a little while I would be OK. The master's daughter must have noticed that I wasn't in the kitchen. She suddenly appeared in the tiny room where I slept.

' "Why aren't you up?" she said accusingly.

' "I'm feeling very ill," I told her. "I just need to rest for a little while and I'll be all right."

' "Get up this minute," she yelled. "Who do you think is going to do the cooking? Why do you think we let you stay here?"

'She was only young, still at school, yet she spoke to me as though I was a small insect. Her mother must have heard the commotion. She appeared in the room. I told her that I was ill and that I could barely move my body.

' "This isn't a resting-home," she mocked. "Get off your backside and get to work."

'I was a very submissive character by this time. It had been beaten into me. I never did anything to displease my employers. But this seemed to be the limit. I was so obviously unwell, yet still they wanted their pound of flesh. I had worked myself into the ground for them without any hope of ever getting paid. I was weary, but I summoned some strength from somewhere.

' "If you can't let me rest for just two hours when I'm clearly ill, give me whatever wages you can and I'll go."

'It's terrible to think that they wouldn't let me rest for one lousy day after all the work that I had done for them. I even used to beg for them. They never had any money and so I always had to beg the vegetable wallah for credit, promising that my master would come along to pay him. But I knew that the promises would never be honoured. One lousy day. That's all that I ever asked for. And not even because I was tired. And so I left with just the one sari that I had been wearing when I left my husband. Was there no happiness for me? Was there nowhere that I could go without receiving insults and abuse for all my hard work? I considered trying to get to Poona in the hope of finding my family, but the fear of my father sending me back to my husband dissuaded me. I considered the other alternatives and decided that I would approach a nice lady who had shown me some kindness when I had run an errand for my master to her house. She had seemed a kind generous lady. I remembered where she lived. It was on the fourth floor of a block of flats. I prayed that she wouldn't turn me away. She answered the door and I could see that she was now pregnant. That little swelling was your sister, Zeeba, and the lady was your mother. She took me into the kitchen and asked me to sit down. She could see that I wasn't well. I explained why I was there. I remember that she asked me just two questions. Was I prepared to work, and was I prepared to travel to Pakistan? I said that I was.

'When I agreed to move to Pakistan I didn't really understand the full implications. But looking back I suppose that that was the time I lost all chance of finding my family again. I was still very young and the thought never occurred to me at the time. I was like an animal in the jungle, fighting for survival every minute of the day, fighting to stay alive. And though it seemed that at last I might be treated with some humanity, it wasn't all smooth running. The lady was a Muslim and the country was in turmoil with religious strife. The lady's husband and brother-in-law didn't want me, a Hindu, in the house. But I agreed to convert, your mother had her way, and I have been with her ever since.'

No one spoke. Laxmi appeared exhausted. It was dark outside now and I could hear the sound of the ocean lapping against the sea-wall below our balcony. But there was something I had to ask.

'How old were you when all this happened, Laxmi?'

'Seven years old. Just seven years old the day that I was led screaming to the altar, my husband leering down at me.'

I Love Lucy

'God created her in his spare time, and with his own hands,' Mrs Sadiq effused. Rakshanda was home from Scotland and Mrs Sadiq was in loquacious tenor. 'Studying for her exams, yet still she has time to buy presents for the tailor's children. Could a mother ask for more than such a child?'

The whole family was gathered for the homecoming. Dr Sadiq smiled genially at his stepdaughter, and Faridoon teased his sister about her Scottish affectations. Fairy Auntie nodded agreement with Mrs Sadiq's every word, for though they were aunt and niece they were in fact more like sisters. Varsy Auntie was helping Zeebande unwrap the gift her sister had bought her. The child's crudely etched WELCOME HOME poster hung on the wall above the mantelpiece, and a table covered with every conceivable chutney, choora, and roti stood in the centre of the lounge. The smell of cooking puri seeped into the room from the kitchen opposite. Only Mrs Shirazi, casting a protective and jealous eye over young Zeebande, and Laxmi, hanging back shyly by the door, ignored the hullabaloo.

'Now you give that doll to Laxmi so that she can put it in your trunk until you're older,' Mrs Sadiq told her youngest daughter. She did not trust the child with the delicate toys that Rakshanda had brought her from Scotland, sure that she would break them. Zeebande was fast accruing a collection of expensive toys that she was unlikely to be allowed the use of until her late teens.

'You know how clumsy you can be? We don't want you to break them, do we?'

It was certainly quite a morning that day when Rakshanda arrived home, what with the food, the drink, and the excitement. By the time she left to visit friends in the early afternoon the adults were glad of an opportunity to sleep. Only little Zeebande remained awake, and denied access to her new toys she had taken solace in the storeroom next to her grandmother's room, her Aladdin's cave of bottles, glasses, cork-stoppers, chemicals, and medicines, all lined neatly on the wooden shelves that her father had had installed for her. Violets, scarlets, turquoises, emeralds, all sparkled in the afternoon sun that sneaked through the tiny window overlooking the patio. Mixing water with iodine, iodine with bromine, bromine with detergent, the louder the colour she could create the happier she was.

Mrs Sadiq had damned her husband as an irresponsible fool the time that he had first brought home his redundant medicines for the child to play with. But when he had suggested that she open the child's trunk of forbidden toys instead, she had settled for the lesser of the two evils. Besides, the doctor had had the good sense to solicit the help of his mother-in-law in ensuring that the child wouldn't test any of her own concoctions. He knew that Zeebande would never disobey her grandmother.

Zeebande was feeding her one-eyed teddy bear a particularly ghastly mixture when I Love Lucy walked into the room. I Love Lucy was the child's pekinese dog, a docile creature that appeared blissfully unaware of the unsuitability of his name. Settling next to the child he looked hungrily at the slice of bread in her hand and accepted it gratefully when it was proffered him. Then, some time around three o'clock when the sun was at its fiercest, Zeebande retreated to her bedroom, and the dog to the lounge.

Dr Sadiq enjoyed the period between 4.30 and five in the afternoon before the rest of the house awoke. He always allowed himself this solitary half-hour with a cup of tea and a newspaper before he set out for his evening surgery. On this particular day he was surprised to find I Love Lucy in the house as his wife usually ensured that he was locked outside, but he allowed the dog to remain in the lounge anyway and together they enjoyed ten minutes of rare silence. But then, as the doctor turned a page of his newspaper, the quietude was shattered by a thunderous roar from the dog's backside, a fart that Dr Sadiq was later to claim lasted a full ten seconds. Fearing the worst, he grabbed the mutt by its collar and dragged it from the room as fast as his delicate heart would allow. He did not care to imagine his wife's reaction if the dog should soil her new woolpile carpet. But he had barely reached the lounge door when the dog let out a vanquished yelp and emptied the contents of its fundament on to Mrs Sadiq's carpet. In his haste to get the dog out of the room the doctor stumbled over Laxmi who had been sleeping in the corner of the room on the floor. She jumped with a start, fearing that Zeebande had placed another cockroach on her stomach, but then hurried to help the doctor clean the mess before Mrs Sadiq awoke. Laxmi's shriek had already awoken her, however, for she had deliberately left the air-conditioning off so that she didn't sleep too deeply. She had Rakshanda's homecoming party to organise that evening and there was plenty of work to be done.

'Aren't I allowed to sleep for five minutes in this house?' she bellowed from her room.

Dr Sadiq was not quick enough to prevent her entering the lounge. She froze at the site of the ugly brown stain on the carpet.

'Where's Rehman?' she demanded.

'I think I saw him out in the garden picking a mango

for the chutney,' her husband advised her, not quite sure what Rehman had to do with anything.

She stormed into the garden nonetheless, and thundered at the cook.

'Sharif Rehman! Get over here.'

Turning from his work he was startled by her tone of voice.

'Yes, Begum Sahib. What is –?'

He wasn't allowed to finish. Raising her voice a semitone with each sentence she continued, 'Is it not enough that I pay you better than any cook in the street? Is it not enough that we give you a place to sleep? Is it not enough that my husband speaks to you as though you were the Governor himself? Don't you think that I know that you water down the milk so that you can take some to that Mrs Adil who I see sneaking into your room late at night? But do I ever say anything? This is the way you repay us?'

Mrs Sadiq's voice had reached the note of F sharp when the cook tried to interject.

'But Begum Sa – '

His interruption increased her fury.

'What kind of man would try to poison my daughter's dog?' she screamed.

Sharif Rehman paled as the gist of Mrs Sadiq's invective hit him.

'What has that dog ever done to you? What has Zeebande ever done to you? What have any of us ever done to you? Is this what we deserve? Will you try to poison us next?'

Mrs Sadiq had exhausted herself and she mellowed a little when she saw a tear appear in the poor man's eye.

'Don't let this happen again. I'll be watching you very closely from now on.'

Rehman was clearly very shaken as the lady returned to the house.

As Zeebande came out of her bedroom after her brief nap she bumped into Laxmi.

'Where's I Love Lucy?' she asked.

'Loosy Boosy Woosy . . .' Laxmi scolded the child, walking past her in deep dudgeon to clean the room. Zeebande knew that Laxmi was angry when she distorted names. Shrugging it off though, she found her father in the lounge reading his paper.

'Will you take me to the surgery tonight?' she asked him.

'Not tonight, bibi. I have a very important call to make afterwards. Perhaps tomorrow.'

'Shall I make you a sandwich to take with you?' she offered.

'That would be nice,' he responded. 'I'll take a shower while you make it.'

When the child returned with the sandwich and the doctor saw the ghastly brown paste spread on the bread, he suggested to her that he might enjoy it more when he got back from work. But the child persisted.

'Take it with you, Daddy. I Love Lucy enjoyed his sandwich this afternoon. You'll like it.'

With a chuckle the doctor picked the child up and placed her on his knee. 'Bibi, I want you to help me put all your medicines in the car. I have to see some very poorly people tonight and I haven't any of my own left. Then I want you to go and find Mr Rehman and tell him that I have an apology to make. Tell him that I will see him later. Run along now while I go to speak to your mother.' He kissed the child as she ran off to the kitchen to find the cook.

'If I hadn't seen her appear from my own body I wouldn't believe that the child was mine,' Mrs Sadiq scolded her husband. 'Just wait until I get my hands on her.'

'No need for that, Chundi Begum. I have already spoken to her and I am afraid I rather lost my temper. I think she has been spoken to severely enough.' The doctor shuffled awkwardly. Lying did not come easily to him. He bade his wife farewell and then left for the surgery.

'I would never harm a dog,' Sharif Rehman muttered to himself as he stirred the biriani. 'I love dogs. I have always loved dogs. Isle of Loo Sea is a nice dog . . .'

School

Miss D'Souza pointed to each letter on the blackboard and took her class of five-year-olds through the English alphabet. Chanting 'A,B,C,D,E,F,G,' they appeared not to notice the old lady with flame-red hair and a bright green sari who was sat beneath a sun-umbrella on the open balcony outside the first-storey classroom reading the cricket scores in the *Daily Jang*.

Dr Sadiq had to admire his mother-in-law's devotion to her granddaughter. He loved Zeebande more than anything else on earth, but Abaji took her love of the child to the limits of absurdity; Zeebande was her all-consuming obsession.

He recalled that on the occasion that he had decided that his daughter should begin her education, her introduction to schooling had not been without difficulties. She was a bright inquisitive child, and he had high hopes that she would follow him into a career in medicine. Both his sons were now doing well for themselves, Jan as a pilot, and Yusuf as a businessman, and he looked forward to the day when all his children were successes in their chosen fields.

So important had he considered Zeebande's schooling that he had fought a successful battle with his wife over the choice of school. He was quietly pleased that his wishes had prevailed, for though his wife's choice, St Joseph's, was undoubtedly a fine school, he feared that his rather sensitive child would not respond well to the disciplined regime on which the school prided itself. Besides, he did not subscribe to his wife's view that anything good enough for 'her children', as she was prone to put it, was good enough for 'his child'. He was satisfied that Happy Hill English School was far more suitable for Zeebande, and its proximity to home would allow him to drop her off himself on his way to the surgery.

Zeebande had developed dreadful stomach pains on the eve of her first day at school, however, and though the doctor had satisfied himself that she had neither a temperature nor tonsillitis, he had nevertheless agreed to delay her induction by a day. She was given green tea by her grandmother and put to bed. The doctor knew that there was not a jot of medicinal value in the tea, but Abaji had convinced the child that it was a magic cure-all, and it therefore served as a useful placebo whenever the child was ill. The pain had occurred shortly after she had been advised by her father that she would not be able to take her two elderly companions along with her to school, that she would be meeting new friends of her own age. She didn't need new friends, she had told him, she already had Nani and Laxmi. Dr Sadiq regretted the position in which his daughter had unwittingly found herself, her sister and brothers all being about four times her own age. In her brief life she had spent far too much time in the company of adults.

On the second day, the child's pains still persisting, Dr Sadiq had gently reproached his wife when she had suggested that Zeebande was feigning illness in order to avoid school. He was in no doubt that the child was genuinely in pain, although he was equally convinced that the illness was psychosomatic and that there was little that any of his medicines could do. However, on the eighth day, returning from his evening surgery, he had crept into her bedroom and sat beside the bed. The child appeared to be asleep.

'Bibi,' he had whispered, stroking her black silk hair.

'One day I want you to be a doctor. One day I want to send you away to London to study so that when I'm old you can look after me. But if you don't go to school, how will you learn? Who'll look after your old dad then?'

The child had opened her eyes and wrapped her arms around his neck.

'I'll study, Daddy,' she had said to him. 'I promise I'll go to school.'

He had smiled with satisfaction, kissed her forehead, and driven to Clifton Beach to buy her a songbird.

Dr Sadiq was examining a rather unpleasant ingrowing toe-nail when his surgery phone rang. He had dropped his daughter at the school gates an hour earlier.

'Doctor! Come quickly!' a distressed female voice had pleaded.

'To whom am I speaking?' he had enquired, the patient's foot in one hand, and the receiver in the other.

'Come quickly! This is the headmistress. Your daughter is very ill.'

Young Zeebande was indeed in the throes of her second fit of vomiting when Mrs Khan had phoned, and the doctor, alarmed and fearing a serious illness, had collected her straight from school and taken her back to the surgery with him. But a thorough check-up once again showed her to be in rude health. A stand would have to be taken, he decided.

On the fourteenth day of Zeebande's education, Dr and Mrs Sadiq were summoned to Happy Hill English School. There had been no improvement in their daughter's condition.

'Double figures she has vomited,' the hysterical headmistress had advised them in her best English. 'It is upsetting the other children,' she had said. 'She must find another school.'

Dr Sadiq was not convinced that a court of law would have upheld vomiting as sufficient grounds to warrant a child's expulsion from school, but he had accepted the lady's wishes in any case. He could not have known at that time that six months later he would have been given the same reason at a further four schools. He hadn't any idea what to do. No amount of coaxing, no extra visits to the paan stall, no amount of gifts showered on her did the trick. His daughter would no sooner step through the gates of a school and see Sultan the driver pull away in the car than she would throw up.

The doctor had been grateful, therefore, when, after the fifth expulsion, his mother-in-law had approached him at supper.

'I can't take any more of this,' she had said. 'The child is ill. She doesn't eat, she doesn't sleep, and she is losing weight. She doesn't even play any more. All her time is spent worrying about school. And her worries are my worries. So give me responsibility for the child. Give me two weeks alone with her, and I shall see that she goes to school.'

He had accepted her wishes without hesitation. His wife had unhelpfully mocked her mother, but no amount of mocking was going to make her daughter a doctor. And so Mrs Shirazi had taken control of her granddaughter's education. For the first two weeks the child and grandmother had barely stepped foot out of the bedroom. They had eaten together, slept together, and talked together. Zeebande had confided to her grandmother that she was not being obstinate, that she really did want to study. She had told her that the vomiting was completely involuntary, and that it was born of a fear of abandonment, of being left alone for ever with strangers, locked inside the school gates. Mrs Shirazi had asked her granddaughter under what circumstances she could imagine herself sitting in class without anxiety.

'If you come with me,' she had immediately replied.

And so, after the child's two-week quarantine, Mrs Shirazi had announced to her daughter and son-in-law that the child would be starting school the next day. She had gained admission for her to a very good school near Soldier Bazaar and had explained to the headmistress about her granddaughter's delicate stomach condition. She had obtained permission to accompany the child to school until such time that she was able to be left alone.

'You're stark raving mad,' her daughter had told her. Dr Sadiq had just chuckled with delight.

On the morning of the third Wednesday in March, Mrs Shirazi and her granddaughter had risen early. They had washed, dressed, packed some sandwiches and orange juice, and had walked past the sneering Mrs Sadiq to the car and driven to St Lawrence's Convent School for Girls. A huge red-brick building, a legacy of the British, it was juxtaposed with a more modern and smaller two-storey building that housed the first-, second- and third-year classes. This odd couple of grandmother and child had climbed the staircase to the first-storey balcony that ran the length of the building and had entered Room 1b before the other children arrived. Mrs Shirazi had spoken to the teacher, Miss D'Souza, a middle-aged lady from Maharashtra, who had allowed her to take one of the tiny wooden seats from the classroom and place it on the balcony outside. As the schoolchildren had filtered into class she had taken the seat, opened her newspaper, and had occasionally looked up and smiled at her granddaughter who was seated at the desk closest to the door. On the second day Mrs Shirazi had taken the precaution of bringing an umbrella with her as protection against the sun. At the end of the first week she had taken Zeebande to her favourite ice-cream parlour on the way home from school.

'Zeeba, rani,' she had said. 'You know how much I love you and that I would be happy to sit on the balcony outside your classroom all my life if that was your wish. But it is very difficult for me to hold on to an umbrella while reading a newspaper at the same time. So would you mind if I sit somewhere else? There is a nice bench underneath the tree below your classroom. I have spoken to Miss D'Souza who says that if you're feeling ill you can look down from time to time to make sure I'm there.'

And so it was that Mrs Shirazi sat beside the frog pond for the next two months in the shade of the guava tree, reading the *Daily Jang*.

'Nani. Can I go to school with Samina tomorrow? She says her father will pick me up in his car on the way.'

The Sadiq household were gathered around the dining-table and Mrs Sadiq had made fish curry as a special treat for her daughter.

'See!' Mrs Shirazi said to her daughter. 'The child is an angel.'

Yes, Dr Sadiq thought to himself. I've got to take my hat off to Abaji. She really does love her granddaughter.

Lame Auntie

Mother let me go to keep Father happy, and Father took me to keep Lame Auntie happy, and I went because I liked to go, though I didn't know where it was I was going nor who it was that I was seeing. Sultan was at the wheel and my father beside me, always beside me, and off we went through the neat well-lit streets off Shaheed-e-Millat Road, the shops shuttered, the streets empty, out towards Qaid-i-Azam Mausoleum illuminated in the blackness, past the squatting Pathans in Jinnah Road and on past the zoo and across the Layari River, the roads getting rougher, the streets getting darker. Every street shall have lighting and a pavement General Ayub Khan had said, but he had forgotten about Goolimar, and he had forgotten about Nazimabad, and he had forgotten about Gharibabad, place of the poor. But we were going to Goolimar to see Lame Auntie, Lame Auntie who wasn't my Auntie, Lame Auntie with the long left leg. On we go but not too fast because I like to gaze at the houses. We move out of the charmless brooding night-time city centre and into the streets of the whores where deep in the darkness women are battered where no one can hear, and mutilated child beggars sleep by the road, legs crushed by their fathers, and into Goolimar where the shops never shut and the poor never sleep, and there are chick-pea-wallahs, aloo-wallahs, kebab-wallahs, tikka-wallahs, juice-wallahs, paan-wallahs, oh so many wallahs. There are makeshift stalls by the dirt-track road where the one-legged Punjabi sells bread, and chairs for the never-ending stream of customers to sit, and naked bulbs strapped to thin bamboo poles which are powered by small generators that stand by each stall, for remember, there is no electricity because General Ayub forgot. I peer from the window at the colours I never see, the noises I never hear, the smells I have never known in the cold antiseptic place where I live – the smell of sewage, the smell of frying, the smell of the poor – and I want to have jalebi and I want to have tikka, but Daddy says Lame Auntie has prepared food, my favourite Lucknowi kebabs and my favourite Lucknowi bread, you will never eat if you eat now, besides, what would your grandmother say, she would never forgive me for buying you street food, but if you're still hungry and you promise not to tell we'll stop on our way home. And so on down the road past the purples and the reds, and the greens and the blues of the gigantic hand-drawn film banners, *The Call from my Heart, My Heart Beats for You, The Love Cage, Desire,* off the main road and Sultan parks the car because the track to Lame Auntie's house is too narrow and bumpy, I know we are nearly there because I can smell the open drain, and I can smell Daddy's Old Spice when I bury my nose in his shirt-sleeve, and then I see it, the white-washed adobe house with the little garden where paan leaves grow, Lame Auntie and her family gathered at the door to greet us. Who is this woman you visit? my mother had complained; my mother's cousin's daughter, I thought he had said, a crisp white bedsheet laid on the charpoy outside, and a small table with pink patterned tablecloth, kebabs marinated in papaya, scented sheer-mal bread melting in the mouth though not in my father's mouth for he can't take spices although he always takes two bites out of courtesy, no Punjabi cooks, no Bengali cooks, just Lucknowi cooks cooking Lucknowi delicacies, ice-cold Coke from the stall down the track, and tea for my father no milk no sugar, and then the table is cleared and the paan leaves produced, Lame

Auntie's paandan placed on the table, the stainless steel container the size of a child's hand with little compartments for the betel-nut and acreca, the lime and the khatha, and a little sugar for Zeeba, the ceremony of the paan. And then I am tired and it's time to go home. I wish I had something to give to Zeeba, she says; are you short of money he says; oh no I couldn't, she says; oh yes you can, he says, squeezing 500 rupees into her hand, I'll see you in a month, he says, and then back home, away from the smells, away from the noise, off the dirt-track and on to the smooth flat streets of Bahadurabad, back from Lame Auntie who isn't my Auntie, Lame Auntie with the long left leg.

… and then the Pickle-Man Came

A hidden chorus of cicadas sang as a ghostly hush settled on the city: Karachi at night. Some neighbours gossiped, drinking tea on their bungalow verandah. Coloured fairy lights flickered in an adjacent street, announcing an impending marriage. My parents were at the Gymkhana Club, an evening at the card table; my brother Farid was with friends; and Rakshanda, my elder sister, was now married. I was alone with my two best friends: my grandmother and Laxmi.

It was eight o'clock, the dining-table had been cleared after supper, and the three of us were settled on the large cream settee in the lounge. Nani had produced an old photograph album, and was leafing through half-forgotten memories. My head cushioned against her shoulder I sat enchanted as she recalled stories of her childhood in Iran, her marriage to the rich merchant from Baghdad, my grandfather, and her many travels between the Middle East and India. But the evening had turned to night and I had school the next day. Concerned that I ought to be in bed she cajoled Laxmi into singing some of the popular songs from the Bombay movies, an attempt to encourage sleep. But they were no lullabies to me, and she was already on her fourth rendition of my favourite 'Love is your Reward' when I caught the sound of a bell ringing in the street. It was a strange foreign sound in the comfortable familiarity of those childhood evenings. Jumping from my seat to investigate I ran into the garden, dragging the hapless Laxmi with me. Down the driveway and through the gateway I turned, looking into the darkness of the street. And there, appearing out of the night, a single brass lantern lighting his way, I saw the pickle-man for the very first time. He was stooped and grey, and he sat perched on a rusting cart, the lantern and bell swinging in rhythm to the laboured lolloping of his donkey. I ran towards him as Laxmi looked cautiously on. He reined in the donkey as I called to him, and easing himself down from his seat he greeted me in broken Urdu. His high cheek-bones and dark skin told me that he was Bengali. There were a thousand wrinkles in his face and a long grey beard reached down to his chest. His gait was unsteady as he took the lantern from its hook and moved round the cart parading his wares: great glass jars of pickled fruits and vegetables. There were small whole lemons pickled in their own juices; green mangoes, unripe and not yet fully grown, pickled in mustard oil and turmeric; whole chillies pickled with cumin and garlic; and his speciality, mixed-pickle, with mangoes, carrots, whole cloves of garlic, chillies, and lemon.

I had been talking to my new friend for about an hour when Nani called me in. Waving him goodbye I made him promise that he would visit me again the next day. True to his word he arrived at exactly the same time the following evening, a pattern he was to repeat every night for the next two months. After supper I would sit by the garden gates waiting for the dim lantern to appear at the top of the street. And then I would make out his grey wrinkled face, and the tired old features of his donkey. There were nights when I couldn't tell them apart; they could have been twins. They would dawdle down the street together, stop beneath the pear tree that overhung the garden wall, and each nod their greeting to me. For the first week Laxmi would hover discreetly by the gates, but once she and my grandmother saw that there was no harm in the old man they left us alone. And it was only then that I was able to taste those wonderful pickles for the very first time, for though I had been allowed to buy them I had never been allowed to eat them. My grandmother was an aristocrat at heart and could not countenance the idea of her granddaughter eating the food of a street-hawker. Her prejudice had been fashioned when she had once seen a nut-seller urinating by the road. But I didn't care. I imagined that I was his only customer, and bought something from him every night. Out of the sight of my grandmother he would give me little samples, and at nine when she called me in he would bid me salaam and I would watch as he disappeared into the darkness of the street, the lamp suspended in the air. And then one night that lamp faded into the distance never to return. Beautiful Karachi nights with Nani, Laxmi, the old man, and the donkey.

I recently reminded my grandmother of the pickle-man, and enquired as to what might have happened to him.

'What pickle-man, Zeeba?' she said. 'We used to make our own pickles.'

The Birthday Party

'She had a black ant in her belly-button,' Dr Sadiq advised the worried guests as he carried his daughter from behind the bushes. 'Please carry on with the party.'

It always rained on 18 July and Zeebande knew it. What bothered her more, though, was that her hair still hadn't grown to the length of Lame Auntie's daughter's, it still wasn't cascading down her back as she had been promised. She had taken the yellow tablets religiously for three months, just as her father had told her, and the sweet orange ones for six: but still it couldn't be plaited. And so, on that morning, the morning of 18 July 1967, her birthday, she confronted her father with the bottles of cod liver oil and Serbax Vitamin C tablets and demanded an explanation.

'Daddy, how can I wear the shalwar kurta that Lame Auntie gave me today if I still have short hair? Appai will make me wear that awful green dress. You will have to give me an injection.'

'Watch your tongue, child,' Mrs Sadiq interjected, walking into the room. 'That's a very expensive dress. What on earth do you want to wear that dreadful red outfit for? First you want long hair like a Hindi, and then you want to dress like a Hindi. You'll end up looking like those Goolimar relatives of your father's.'

Dr Sadiq parried his wife's insults with his usual good humour.

'Come on, bibi. I'll drop you off at the hairdresser's on my way to work. Let's see what they can do with your hair.'

And so, breakfast finished, the child followed her father to the car, and two hours later returned home with an outrageous bouffant set that added a full five inches to her height. Her mother nearly wept.

The rain had cleared by lunchtime and the trees and flowers looked smarter for their dowsing. Preparations for the party had begun, the electricians weaving flex through the branches of the trees for the coloured fairy lights, and the caterers setting up the charcoal barbecues on the back patio outside the kitchen. Mrs Shirazi was attending the van-load of hired chairs that had just arrived, directing that most be placed in the garden, and the rest on the patio in the event of rain. The makeshift stage was already erected, ready for the music and wrestling later that night. Dr and Mrs Sadiq were inside, at the lunch table with their young daughter.

'Zeebande, you are five years old today. You are a little lady now,' her mother said to her sternly.

The child glowed. At last she was a lady, just like her sister.

'But I want you to remember that little ladies don't ask their guests what gifts they have bought them before they have even had a chance to step through the gates.'

Mrs Sadiq tried not to smile, but her husband was a little less inhibited and burst out laughing.

'Don't encourage her, Sadiq. She knows few enough manners as it is,' she chastised her husband. 'Now, go and give your green dress to Laxmi to iron,' she continued, turning to her daughter again.

Zeebande's mood changed instantly and her father was quick to sense it.

'Let her wear Lame Auntie's suit for just a couple of hours before the guests arrive,' he coaxed his wife. 'She'll change into her dress later – won't you, bibi?'

'Just so long as the little madam knows that my idea

of a good time is not traipsing round children's boutiques in the July heat. It cost me 200 rupees, that dress.'

'Give it a rest, Appai,' Rakshanda scolded her mother as she walked into the room, returning home early from college. 'Let her enjoy her birthday.'

Mrs Sadiq melted like butter. Rakshanda was now eighteen years old and her mother was putty in her hands. Though she was not to know it at the time, it was to be the last occasion that Rakshanda would be in attendance for the family photograph, and in future years Zeebande would face the embarrassment of explaining to her friends why her mother was holding a photograph of Rakshanda aloft above her head in the traditional birthday photograph.

'Come on, Zeebande,' Rakshanda said. 'I'll help you to change. You'll look lovely in your little red suit.'

'She'll look lovely in her little red dress,' Mrs Sadiq echoed, turning to her husband.

The party was in full swing. The barbecue spat fat from the mutton, quail, and chicken cooking on the charcoal as Laxmi threw the spices into the flames. 38 Bahadurabad sparkled like a Harrods festive display. Dr Sadiq served the guests from behind his custom-made mahogany bar, while his wife and her friends watched the harmonium and tabla players pack their instruments before the wrestling began. A slight, unobtrusive individual stood alone in the half-light by the gates, dressed in an ill-fitting grey suit, and looking decidedly uncomfortable. It was Jaffna, Dr Sadiq's younger brother, Mrs Sadiq's one concession to her husband's relatives. Kind and sensitive, he suffered from permanent ill-health, and he wouldn't allow his brother to buy him clothes, only accepting his cast-offs reluctantly. He felt conspicuous among the well-to-do guests.

At eleven the wrestlers took the stage; Gamma Pahelwan, a baby-faced nineteen-year-old who hadn't lost a bout, and Qalu Dada, a twenty-seven-year-old giant, but in effect a no-hoper against the precocious talent of his young opponent. Dr Sadiq watched his wife in deep confabulation with Naseem Hassan, her wealthy cousin from Lahore. He was puzzled that she had been invited as his wife avowedly despised her. But Mrs Sadiq had her motives.

'Find me a giant who can't fight,' she had instructed the agent who had arranged the bout. She had obtained generous odds from her cousin who wasn't aware of Gamma Pahelwan's reputation and Mrs Sadiq had staked a little more money than she ought to have done. But it seemed money well invested when, a little later, Gamma held his opponent in a winning stranglehold.

'One . . . two . . .' the referee counted.

The scream from behind the bushes cut him short and as the startled Gamma Pahelwan loosened his grip momentarily his opponent seized his opportunity.

'One . . . two . . . three. The winner is Qalu Dada.'

Qalu punched the air in triumph, but his audience paid him no heed as they peered beyond the stage into the bushes. There was thunder in Mrs Sadiq's eyes as her husband carried Zeebande out in his arms in her bright red suit.

'She had a black ant in her belly-button,' the doctor explained.

Zeebande, her brass pots having been sequestered by her mother, had been squatting in the bushes away from the frogs when she had been attacked by a large black ant that had climbed the leg of her kurta and settled itself in her navel.

'I have never seen the child before,' Mrs Sadiq stormed. 'I do not know her. I demand a re-fight.'

Ali Agh

'Who was Ali Agh?' I asked my grandmother.

'Ali Agh was a snake who wouldn't piss on your chopped finger,' she replied.

I had never particularly wanted Ali Agh to piss on my chopped finger, but I took her point.

'It was Ali Agh who squandered our family fortune. If it hadn't been for Ali Agh your mother and I could be living in comfort during our old age instead of having Mrs Malik stumbling round the house drunk every night.'

Ali Agh had fascinated me since I was a small child. Ali Agh of the vituperative scorn of my grandmother, Ali Agh of the sapphire eyes, Ali Agh of the forbidden room. If you go into Ali Agh's room you'll never come out again, my great-grandmother used to warn me.

'At the time that my grandfather decided to leave India and return to Iran his business hadn't been doing too well,' Nani continued. 'He was disaffected by India and wanted to return home as quickly as possible. My father, who had a small business of his own, took the ailing concern off his hands when he married my mother. He worked hard and turned the business round, and by the time he decided to start a family he was quite a wealthy man. I grew up wanting for nothing.

'Apart from his own family my father also supported his sister, Zehra, and his wastrel of a half-brother, Ali Agh. Ali Agh had been disowned by his father, tired of his philandering and indolence. But my father was a loyal man, and on the death of their father had arranged a generous monthly allowance for his brother. Ali Agh therefore continued life in the style to which he had become accustomed. Always immaculately dressed, and always in the latest fashions, he carried an ornamental walking stick wherever he went. With a handle the shape of a lion's head and sapphire eyes to match his own, it had been bought for him by his adoring sister, Zehra. He moved in the exclusive British circles to which my father had introduced him, and with his charm and charisma ruined many a stable marriage among the memsahibs. But my father had a reputation to maintain, and fearful that his brother's antics were getting a little out of hand he bought him a Hindu slave-girl for 100 rupees. She was called Diluwaz, and after converting to Islam she moved into Zehra's home as a sop to Ali Agh's sexual appetite. She could never hope for marriage, of course, but she was treated well and eventually bore him a son, Ahmed. She still quietly nurtured dreams of marriage, however, but those dreams died the day that my own father died. His body was barely in the ground when my mother received a proposal of marriage from Ali Agh.

'I never forgave her for marrying him, for marrying the man who had bribed a government official to transfer all the deeds of my father's business to his own name during my father's final illness, leaving us with nothing when he eventually died. Luckily, a judge was less easy to bribe and the estate was returned to my mother when Ali Agh was hauled before the courts. But then, having established our rights to the legacy, the silly woman agrees to marry him.

'You need a father,' she told us. I certainly didn't need him. I despised the man. But she married him anyway, and within a few years he had squandered every last penny of the inheritance, seducing my sister along the way, his own niece. So you see, don't ever doubt that

Ali Agh was a snake in the grass who wouldn't piss on your chopped finger.'

Biboo Bai

Hashim the jeweller winced with pain as Dr Sadiq released the left testicle that he had cradled in his hand, startled at his daughter's sudden and untimely intrusion. The child had never grasped the formal intimacy of a doctor's surgery and so never thought to knock when she was excited. Hashim didn't know whether to be relieved or hurt as the child marched straight past him and jumped into the brown leather chair behind the desk.

'Daddy, can we have shahi breakfast at the Moghul of Hotels tomorrow?' she gushed excitedly.

The doctor composed himself and turned to his patient.

'Hashim, I shall speak to the hospital tomorrow. You have a hernia.' And then turning to his daughter, 'Bibi, can you go and get your daddy an ice-cream from next door while Mr Hashim changes.'

The child took some money from her father and when she returned Hashim was gone.

'Bibi, I want you to promise me that you won't ever barge into my surgery again without knocking. You know that I don't mind. You know that I would be with you every minute of the day if I could. But Mr Hashim was very embarrassed.' Sternness did not come easily to the doctor. 'Now, what were you telling me about breakfast?'

Zeebande's source of excitement had been the soon-to-be-opened Shahbaz Hotel that she and Sultan had passed on the way to the surgery. 'Come, brothers, come one and all,' the young teenage boy had declaimed outside the shuttered shop next door to Mateen's Sports Store. 'Shahi breakfast fit for a king,' he had called. 'Free halwa with potato puri for our first thirty customers.'

'Bibi, if you make me a promise that you will always knock in future, I shall take you for breakfast.'

He was both charmed and appalled by his daughter's predilection for street food, knowing full well that the new venue was neither a hotel nor restaurant, but a workman's tea-house. The child promised readily.

As good as his promise, Dr Sadiq woke his daughter early the following morning for shahi breakfast. It was a chilly morning and the child was wrapped in a double layer of clothes by her grandmother.

'Make sure it's clean before you let her eat,' she growled at her son-in-law.

The Shahbaz Hotel stood on the main road opposite the Soldier meat and vegetable bazaar, and had already attracted a sizeable mixture of market traders and beggars for its generous opening offer. The doors were not yet open and as the car pulled into the parking-bay Dr Sadiq and his daughter were greeted by a swarm of beggars. 'Why does she bring me to these places?' the doctor groaned to himself.

'Shall I get Sultan to bring the food to the car?' he asked his daughter.

'Can we eat inside, please?' she begged her father.

Dr Sadiq didn't suppose that any of the customers would ever have seen a woman or child in such an establishment before. He acceded to her wishes, however, but no sooner had they taken a few tentative steps through the throng of beggars than a voice thundered from the direction of the 'Hotel'.

'Sahib! Dr Sadiq, isn't it?'

The doctor looked around, puzzled. He couldn't imagine that he would know anyone there.

'Well, I never,' the voice continued. 'What a small world it is that we're living in.'

The voice belonged to a short, thickset man of about fifty, dressed in a white vest and dhoti, sitting behind a huge cauldron of bubbling potato sabzi. He jumped from his perch outside the Hotel and greeted the bemused doctor.

'Allah is surely smiling on my kismet today. Dr Sadiq attends my opening. It is an omen. For sure my business will be a success now. Oh, Doctor, we had such good times, didn't we? You and me, the terrible twins!'

The doctor didn't know who on earth the man was. He recognised a Lucknowi accent but struggled to remember the splendid times that he had allegedly shared with this breakfast-wallah.

'Come in, come in. How rude of me, making you stand outside among this riff-raff,' the man proclaimed haughtily, brushing through the expectant throng. The restaurant was not yet open and the doctor and his daughter were offered their choice of seats. The proprietor was going to savour every moment of his undoubted beneficence in offering the free breakfasts and had no intention of opening until there was a crowd of at least two hundred outside.

'Well, well, well. Who would have thought, eh, Doctor? After all these years.'

'Yes, it's good to see you again, my good man.' The doctor shifted uneasily in his seat. 'I wonder if I might have some potato puri for my daughter, Mr . . .?'

The proprietor shook his head from side to side in realisation, a smile breaking out across his face.

'You don't recognise me do you, Doctor Sahib? You don't recognise me but you're far too polite to say. Biboo Bai!'

Dr Sadiq froze at the mention of that name.

'Biboo Bai!' his new-found friend repeated. 'You remember Biboo Bai? I was her harmonium player.'

'Then you must be Ghulam N –'

'That's right, Doctor,' the harmonium player interrupted. 'Ghulam Nabi at your service.'

Biboo Bai, the doctor thought to himself. Who would have thought that I would ever hear that name again?

'Laloo,' Ghulam called to the young boy busying himself behind the counter. 'Bring hot, hot cup of tea for my friend Doctor Sahib, and cold, cold glass of milk for baby.'

The doctor had by now recovered his composure.

'So what brings you to Karachi, Ghulam?' he asked.

'Well, many tales to tell, Doctor, but I wasn't getting any younger and when I emigrated to Pakistan I thought, new country, new life. I had some money put by from my years in Biboo's employment and so I bought myself this little place. I had married a beautiful girl from Benares and decided that it was time to settle down. So here I am. Not rich, but happy. And today you have honoured me with a visit on our grand opening. We've just given the place a face-lift, you see. Besides,' he smiled, patting his considerable paunch, 'I'm a little too much of an eyesore these days for Biboo's golden voice. What happy days those were, eh, Doctor?'

He felt a lump in his throat thinking of Biboo Bai again. He had been the dashing young man in town in those days. Studying medicine in England by that time, he was heralded as something of a playboy on his visits home to Lucknow. And then he had fallen in love with the beautiful ghazal singer, and she with him. But it was never to be. His life was in England, and hers in Lucknow.

'You know, Doctor, for many years after you left she dedicated ghazals to you. She sold her studio pining for you.'

The doctor felt sad. Certainly his life had been a good one and he could not complain. But difficult as it was to admit, he still held a torch for Biboo Bai.

'Tell me, Ghulam, whatever happened to Biboo? Is she still in Lucknow?' He tried to sound as casual as possible.

'Doctor!' Ghulam exclaimed, genuinely startled. 'You mean that you don't know? I am shocked.' He paused for effect. 'Biboo is in Karachi. We travelled here together. It is here that we went our separate ways. She lives in the end bungalow down Breeze Lane in Nazimabad. She lives there with her sister. You remember little Bilquis? She was only a titch of a girl at the time.'

Of course he remembered Bilquis. He remembered every minute that he had spent in that place.

'I am ashamed to say, Doctor, that it has been some time since I saw Biboo myself. I have a young daughter now and it wouldn't be seemly for me to be seen at her house, no matter how great a singer she was.'

The doctor's heart was heavy, though he tried not to show it. He recalled those days in his beloved Lucknow when he and his friend Wajahat had dreamed of being wandering Urdu poets. Wajahat had indeed gone on to greater things in Indian cinema while the doctor himself had occasionally slipped in a few verses on radio when he was working for the BBC World Service during his breaks in study. It was Wajahat, in fact, who had first taken him to Biboo's studio on one of his visits home. That night he had fallen in love with the beautiful ghazal singer and her magical voice, and every night for the rest of his stay he had wandered through the back streets of Lucknow to the Street of the Kings where he had paid court to the beautiful Biboo. Had it been true, the story that he heard many years later, that Biboo had never married, that she had lost her heart to a doctor in

England? He didn't doubt it, for it had been Wajahat who had told him. Wajahat and Sadiq; they had been inseparable. How could they have imagined then that they were eventually fated to marry the same woman. The first time that the doctor had met Mrs Sadiq she and Wajahat were entertaining in Bombay. He had been there on business. 'This is my best and oldest friend,' Wajahat had announced the doctor. His future wife had smiled at him demurely. 'This is the man who broke the heart of the famous Biboo Bai, the man for whom she still sings her ghazals.'

'You exaggerate, old man,' the doctor had replied, admiring his friend's choice of wife.

The sudden rush of customers into the restaurant woke the doctor from his reverie.

'Yes, Ghulam, those were certainly good days.'

'Where's your father?' Mrs Sadiq asked Zeebande. 'He ought to be back by now.'

'I think he said that he was going to see Biboo Bai,' her daughter answered clumsily.

Mrs Sadiq stiffened.

'Who is Biboo Bai?' she asked, not very convincingly. Mrs Sadiq had wondered how long it would be before her husband discovered that the singer was in town.

The Face after the Moon

My mother never looked at the moon. No one remembers when it started, nor why. But oh, the imprecations and the curses, the spells to be cast and the prayers to be said should the moon ever surprise her from behind the buildings and trees. Caught among the late-night shoppers down Tariq Road I would cling to her handbag, cowering with shame as she froze, standing stock-still, eyes tight shut, calling for her faithful talisman: Rakshanda the beautiful; Rakshanda the beloved; Rakshanda, the face after the moon. Rooted to the pavement, she would not budge until my sister was called. She would place her hands on Rakshanda's head in supplication, and chant senseless Arabic incantations as I hid my face from the bemused crowds around us. And then, only then, would she open her eyes to the face after the moon and continue with her shopping, dragging me behind her, as I fought back my tears and wondered why I could never, not once, be the face after the moon.

Masroor Varsy was an ugly boy and Mrs Sadiq was not enamoured of her daughter's friendship with this child of Delhi johnny-come-latelys. He was dark-skinned, buck-toothed, and had a wide cavernous mouth – not what she had had in mind for her beautiful daughter. What had the Hussains been thinking of, inviting such a boy to their daughter's eighteenth birthday party? The children of all the best families in Karachi were there and Mrs Sadiq had been full of hope that her daughter might meet a nice boy; a good boy, with good prospects. Look at Ali Akbar's son for instance. He had impeccable manners and a bright future, yet Rakshanda had shown no interest when he had called with his parents one evening. And she had been downright rude to Amar Chowdhury when he had brought flowers round one day after meeting her at the Gymkhana Club. Where did Rakshanda find her taste in boys? What had possessed her to bring this boy to Zeebande's party when there were so many others to choose from?

Mrs Sadiq had known that the portents were not good when Laxmi had announced a Mr and Mrs Varsy the day after Zeebande's party.

'Who?' she had lied, knowing full well who, and most probably why.

'Masroor's parents,' Laxmi had offered helpfully. 'Rakshanda's friend at the party.'

Laxmi had ushered the guests into the lounge while Dr Sadiq was called, Mrs Varsy waif-like and fragile like a bird, with a serpentine plait which stretched to the carpet, and Mr Varsy, a little too self-important for Mrs Sadiq's liking.

'What an unsuited couple,' Mrs Sadiq had mocked later, stung by the cheek of the Varsys' proposal. 'Him with his long Sherwani jacket, and her with those tight Delhi pyjamas and brocaded shirt. Where do the Hindis find their taste in clothes? Did you see that awful gold and silver? They don't seem to feel dressed unless they have a thousand sequins splashed down their shirts. They look like those musicians you hired for the party, Sadiq. I thought the woman was going to break into song when she walked into the lounge. Shemsun sister indeed! No daughter of mine is going to be paraded with the pearly queen of Delhi!'

Rakshanda announced her engagement to Masroor the day after Mrs Sadiq had thought that she had seen off the Varsy challenge. Masroor had swallowed a handful of Valium tablets when his parents had conveyed Mrs Sadiq's reaction to their proposal but, in his haste to shovel them down, had heaved them straight back up. Thus convinced of his devotion, Rakshanda had accepted his proposal against the wishes of her mother. Dr Sadiq had ventured the opinion that the youngsters would make a fine couple, but his observation had been brushed aside with disparaging disdain by his wife. Even so, Mrs Sadiq now sensed that she had a fight on her hands.

'Don't make the same mistake that I did, my darling,' Mrs Sadiq pleaded with her daughter. 'Look at the trouble I had with your father. Don't worry about that nasty business. It doesn't matter that you're not a virgin. You were raped, my love. I never did trust that Zahir boy. I should never have allowed you to go to his party. I shall rip him apart with my bare hands if he ever sets foot in this city again. But these are modern days, Rakshanda. It's only the stupid Hindis who still view the cloth of the blooded virgin. There's no need to go off with the first person who asks. Why tie yourself to a boy of twenty, and an ugly boy at that? He hasn't even finished his studies yet. I was naive and stupid when I married your father. I was young, and didn't know better. But you're different. With your beauty and intelligence you'll be able to choose any man you like when you're a little older. They'll be falling at your feet. I didn't listen to your grandmother when we had this same conversation all those years ago and I suffered as a consequence. So don't be hasty. Don't marry the first boy who takes an overdose. How can such a boy realise the implications of marriage? Think carefully. It's the rest of your life that you're deciding.'

'I'll think about it, Appai,' sighed Rakshanda, moving towards her room.

'And, Rakshanda!' her mother called after her. 'Please stop asking your sister to swear into the tape-recorder. It may amuse her father, but you're eighteen years old now. We don't want people to think that we bring our children up like Hindis.'

Rakshanda turned and smiled. Later that day she telephoned Masroor and called off their engagement.

After lunch the table was quickly cleared. Ashtrays, plastic chips, and four brand-new packs of cards were placed in the centre. The guests began to arrive at 2.30, and by three the game was under way. Mrs Malik, Mrs Razak, Mr and Mrs Qadir, Mrs Sadiq, and Mrs Shirazi all sat around the table, each with a neat pile of chips before them. At four they were disturbed by a ringing on the doorbell, and when the noise persisted Mrs Sadiq called to Laxmi.

'Laxmi! Get rid of them. Tell them no one's in.'

The game continued, but just as suddenly as the ringing had stopped, the door to the lounge burst open and a dishevelled, frantic Masroor Varsy stumbled into the room. He headed straight for Mrs Sadiq and hurled himself at her feet. The shock of the assault sent a straight flush flying from her hands and the boy sat on the eight of spades as he embraced her legs and wrapped his feet round the table leg.

'Full house!' shouted Mrs Malik, triumphantly fanning her cards across the table.

'Let go, child!' cried Mrs Sadiq, trying to kick her legs free.

'I shall not move from this spot until I am promised the hand of your daughter,' wailed the boy, gripping tighter.

'He must love her,' observed Mrs Qadir to her husband.

'Cut for seat,' suggested Mrs Razak, eager to start a new game.

'Are you all going mad?' cried Mrs Sadiq. 'There's a boy at my feet. Sadiq! Sadiq! Get in here. There's a madman in the house.'

Dr Sadiq had already heard the commotion and woken from his nap. Seeing Rakshanda's stepfather enter the room, the young Varsy called to him.

'Doctor. I shall throw myself in front of a train if I am not allowed the hand of Rakshanda in marriage.'

The doctor smiled. He had said the same thing to Mrs Sadiq when she had first spurned his advances. He liked Masroor as he had taken the trouble to introduce himself at Zeebande's party.

'Come on, Mr Varsy. Let's leave the guests to their game. We'll go to the kitchen and talk it over, man to man.'

He led the boy to the kitchen where he poured two large scotches.

'Son, I think that you would make a fine husband for Rakshanda,' he consoled him. 'But you must understand that it was her own decision. It is her that you must persuade, not us . . .'

Masroor Varsy left the house ten minutes later.

'He's from Delhi,' Mrs Sadiq offered by way of explanation to her guests as they heard the front door slam shut.

The day after the card game Rakshanda accosted her mother at the breakfast table. News had travelled fast.

'Appai. I shall marry Masroor, and that is my final word on the matter,' she announced.

'May the gods preserve us,' her mother was heard to proclaim as she thudded to the floor in a hot faint.

Babu

'How many times were you married, Nani?' I asked my grandmother.

'Twice,' she answered.

'No, you weren't,' I challenged her.

'Yes, of course I was,' she countered. 'Mohamed Ali and Mohsin. You remember Mohsin?'

'What about Babu?'

'Who told you about Babu?'

'Appai.'

'Appai's got a big mouth.'

'Why did you never tell me about him?'

She hesitated.

'I was ashamed, beti. He was the only man that I ever loved, but I was ashamed of him. We're a family of snobs you see, Zeeba. Your mother's a snob, I'm a snob, and your great-grandmother was a snob.

'Babu was a taxi-driver. Many years ago we had been childhood sweethearts, but as our families were from different backgrounds there was no possibility of it going any further. Ours was a prosperous Persian trading family, and his were simple Hindi workers. But he was an honourable man, and years later when he heard that I had lost my husband and that my child would be born without a father, he offered his hand in marriage. I was in no position to reject him, and in any case I had always loved him. Your mother couldn't have wished for a better stepfather. He was kind, loving, and humble, never forgetting that he had married above his station. He took your mother to school every day, picked her up every day, and gave in to her every whim. Once she forgot her lunch-box so he took it along to the school and waited by the gates until lunchtime. He eventually spotted some of her school-mates and asked them to call her for him. He explained that he was her driver and had come to deliver her lunch-box. When your mother came out and saw him she rushed towards him and jumped into his arms, announcing to all that could hear that he wasn't her driver at all, that he was her father, and that yes, he did drive a taxi, but that she didn't care.

'I threw all that away though, threw it all away for that snake Mohsin. Mohsin was a young army captain at the time and he swept me off my feet. He was Persian, someone I could be seen with at parties. I had no hesitation in accepting his proposal of marriage. And that was the biggest mistake that I ever made. That's why I've never spoken of it to you. I was foolishly ashamed of Babu, and I have been ashamed of what I did to him ever since.'

Bashi Mamoo

I never knew who he was, but he was as much a feature of our Thursday evenings as my grandmother's dolma and maas. His Bombay street Urdu suggested that he was perhaps some baggage left over from my mother's Bombay days, and I often imagine that my grandmother and mother saw in him a fellow soul, like them an outsider in Pakistan. He enjoyed in our household a parity with the women that no other male seemed to share, and it was a testament to my family's indulgence that he was able to survive in that strange household where others so easily perished.

Zeebande had been practising all week, and by Thursday afternoon she was quite satisfied that she had perfected the technique. She wasn't yet able to reproduce the full dynamic range mastered by Bashi Mamoo, nor the explosive force with which he announced his post-potatory fulfilment. But she was in her own way now able to reproduce that gastric belch that invariably concluded the Thursday afternoon tea ceremony, and looked forward to demonstrating so.

She was the first to greet Bashi when he wandered into the driveway that particular Thursday. It had just turned five and she had been watching from her bedroom window since four, though Bashi would never have dreamed to arrive so early, disturbing the Sadiq siesta.

'Do you want a cup of tea?' the young child gushed excitedly. 'I'll make it.'

Bashi smiled indulgently at the child as she tugged at his sleeve, his clothes rattling like agitated wind-chimes.

'Come in, Bashi old man,' Dr Sadiq called from the doorway. 'I'm just off to the surgery. The ladies are indoors.'

Bashi moved towards the doctor, hand outstretched, as Zeebande fell into line behind him, aping his curious gait, his spine arched backwards like a pregnant woman, his two huge feet set at a permanent ten to two angle. Laxmi, who had been alerted by the child's shrieks of delight, pretended not to notice and scuttled to the kitchen to make tea. The doctor chuckled.

Bashi was in every way an enigma to Zeebande, a story-book character. He wasn't family that she was aware of, and he had no family of his own. She didn't know where he lived, though she knew that there was an open invitation for him to join them at Bahadurabad, and she could never place the strange idiom in which he spoke, part Urdu, part Persian, and part a language that appeared to be of his own invention.

He was odd-looking, of indeterminate age, though his permanent grey five o'clock shadow suggested that he was nearer her father's age than her mother's. His nose started orthodoxly at the eyeline before flowering into a bulbous tip that very nearly reached to his upper lip. At a 45 degree angle to this nose a biri would invariably be perched between his lips, though seldom lit, and an antique pair of glasses balanced improbably on the nose, one arm long since broken and replaced by a sturdy elastic band that he somehow managed to manoeuvre round his right ear. Bashi Mamoo always wore pyjamas, ill-fitting and hoisted a good four inches above his ankles, and a long white shirt guarded by two sturdy waistcoats. It is entirely conceivable that Bashi's unorthodox walk was a counter to the weight contained in the pockets and lining of those waistcoats, for they accommodated a veritable warehouse of watches, lighters, pens, cigarette holders and rings that he hawked around the streets of the city each day. An additional array of watches was always hidden under the long loose sleeves of his shirt. 'These are my bread and butter,' he used to tell Zeebande as she gazed wide-eyed at this mobile market stall.

'Can I have tea too?' Zeebande asked ten minutes later as Laxmi poured from the delicate china pot.

'You don't like tea, beti,' her Nani interrupted as she stirred sugar into her own cup.

'I do today,' the child countered cussedly, knowing that she would get her way.

'Just a small one then.'

The child took her cup and saucer to the corner of the lounge where she had earlier been playing with her oil paints, a position where she could remain out of sight of her mother and grandmother who were sitting on the sofa with their backs to her. She was, however, in direct line of vision of Bashi who was sitting opposite his two friends in his favoured wicker chair.

Mrs Shirazi drank delicately from her cup, pinching the handle between thumb and first finger, the little finger tilted at an angle in the air. Mrs Sadiq lit a cigarette, waiting for hers to cool; she never liked her tea too hot. Bashi's method was entirely his own, however. He scooped five spoonfuls of sugar into his cup, stirred it, and then emptied its contents into the saucer that he held in his left hand. Lifting the saucer to his mouth he slurped the tea in greedy mouthfuls. The two women seemed impervious to the frightful noise that accompanied the ritual. Behind them Zeebande repeated the motion with her own tea, though wisely eliminating the sound effects. Bashi Mamoo saw her and smiled, exaggerating the noise for her benefit with each subsequent slurp.

It was an odd scene at 38 Bahadurabad that day, Mrs Sadiq and Mrs Shirazi indulging in polite conversation with their ill-bred guest while he gulped the contents of his saucer like a Mirpuri labourer, the young child enjoying herself in silent imitation in the corner of the lounge, and Laxmi seeing everything but saying nothing as she hovered round the room in discreet obedience.

It was after ten minutes, the contents of his crockery empty and a brief lull in the conversation, that Bashi Mamoo, in time-honoured fashion announced his satisfaction with Laxmi's unrivalled tea with a roaring eructation that left the three ladies as unmoved as had his earlier slurping. Indeed, so impassive to this display of primeval vulgarity were the three ladies that Mrs Sadiq, her tea now having cooled sufficiently, felt able to reach forward for her own cup without the slightest hint of nausea. It was while the cup balanced briefly in her hand that from behind her came another frightful belch that caught her quite unawares and caused her momentarily to loosen her grip on the cup which crashed to the floor, splintering into a hundred small pieces around the room. She swung round, following the direction of the noise, and saw her youngest child smiling proudly at the tea-leaves at the bottom of her own empty cup.

My mother must have caught me at a weak moment when she rang this evening. She is made of sterner stuff than myself and was annoyed that I couldn't speak for my tears. Bashi Mamoo died, alone, at nine o'clock this morning.

Baba Jin

Dr Sadiq never drank water. He had tried it once, boiled, sterilised, and then chilled, but he still suffered from diarrhoea for two days. But now he studiously poured himself a tumbler from the jug in the fridge.

'Drinking water, Sadiq?' his wife said smugly as she passed through the kitchen to the back of the house.

'Yes, Begum,' the doctor confirmed, smiling even more smugly than his wife. He was gloating, which was unusual for him.

'Baba Jin will be visiting us the day after tomorrow,' Mrs Sadiq advised her husband.

'Have we met?' he asked, knowing full well that they hadn't. He would never have countenanced a friend with such a name.

'I would be grateful if you could make yourself scarce when he calls, Sadiq.' Her request was sufficiently hesitant to convince Dr Sadiq that his wife was not entirely sure of her ground.

'And who is this Baba Jin?' he enquired.

'Baba Jin's fame is known throughout the continent,' she said, 'and he has travelled all the way from Mysore to be with the faithful in Karachi. Baba Jin talks to the spirits and can see the future. Don't you know anything, Sadiq?'

'Am I to take it that you have invited this lunatic to our house?' the doctor asked.

'Infidel!' she snorted. 'He is doing me the honour of blessing our house.'

'You know, Chundi Begum, I don't know why I have

spent all these years studying and practising medicine. I should have been better served composing senseless invocations, and deceiving gullible fools like yourself.'

He turned to his mother-in-law.

'I take it that you don't approve of this nonsense, Abaji?'

'Son, a dog with a curly tail can place a brick on it for a hundred years, but the tail will remain curly.'

'Scoff if you like,' Mrs Sadiq defended herself. 'Baba Jin will bless this house. Laxmi!' she called. 'We shall need food for twenty guests the day after next.'

Dr Sadiq shook his head wearily and left for the surgery.

Despite her assertions, Mrs Sadiq had never actually heard of Baba Jin until the previous day when Mrs Razak, the wife of the upholsterer, had told her of the magician in town. Mrs Sadiq had lost no time in seeking him out therefore, and had requested that he honour her with a visit. The appointment was confirmed and instructions issued. If the Baba sensed any uncleanliness he would not enter the house, she was told. On the eve of the visit therefore, Mrs Sadiq ordered that the walls and the floors of the house be scrubbed clean, and the next morning she rose early to personally supervise the cooking of a huge biriani for the twenty-five guests.

'Mummy, Baba needs your room,' Mrs Sadiq advised her mother.

'Tell Baba to bugger off,' she responded, although, truth to tell, the particular Persian curse that she used actually made mention of the Baba and a donkey.

'I will ask Baba to forgive you,' Mrs Sadiq retorted.

'Baba can go to hell. What on earth do you need my room for? There are six other rooms in the house.'

'Mama, don't you understand? Yours is the only room where alcohol has never been drunk. Baba has a sensitive nose.'

Knowing that there was a small bottle of brandy in her medicine cabinet, Mrs Shirazi deferred to her daughter's wishes. Let's see if the Baba sniffs that one out, she congratulated herself. Indeed, the medicine cabinet was the only piece of furniture left in the room by the time her daughter had cleared it for disinfecting. The walls and floor were scrubbed, white sheets were placed across the rug, and joss-sticks were lit by the window. A brand-new single mattress was bought for the Baba, and as required by his instructions, rose-petals were scattered around the room.

At mid-afternoon Baba Jin arrived with a flourish. Stepping from a vulgar green Mercedes he was escorted to the house by two young acolytes no more than sixteen years in age and dressed in expensive white saris.

'Step aside, mortals! The procession of the spirits has begun,' they instructed the guests as they rushed towards the car to see the Baba emerge.

Baba Jin had a full head of curly black hair, and a neatly clipped beard. He wore an inappropriate kaftan, with two sets of red and brown beads around his neck. He carried a set of rosary beads in one hand, and what appeared to be a feather duster in the other. He wore open sandals on his feet, and Mrs Shirazi was later to swear that she had noticed pink varnish on his toe-nails, though Mrs Sadiq refuted this suggestion. The procession passed down the hallway to Mrs Shirazi's room, and Mrs Sadiq was forced to slam the door of the lounge shut as she spotted her husband ostentatiously drinking a scotch. He had decided that he wasn't going to be driven from his house by some religious charlatan, and had deliberately returned home early from his surgery.

'I shall require complete silence,' Baba Jin informed his audience, sitting cross-legged on the mattress. 'The spirits do not like noise,' he added by way of amplification. With these words he threw his head back, rolled his eyes upwards in their sockets, began swaying from side to side chanting, 'Haq Allah, Haq Allah,' and then lurched his body forward before springing back into an upright position. His young disciples looked on in humble devotion, while the lady guests watched in awe. Then, suddenly stiffening, he pointed at Mrs Malik who had arrived late and had settled in by the door. She had just returned from an assignation with her lover and had encountered heavy traffic on the way.

'The spirits do not approve of your behaviour,' he reproached her. His disciples nodded. Mrs Malik's friends coughed in embarrassment, while Mrs Sadiq beamed with delight. So Baba Jin really did talk to the spirits!

'Silence!' cried the Baba. 'Don't disturb the spirits, sisters,' he explained, rolling his head in an anti-clockwise motion. 'I can feel an aura in this house. And the spirits are telling me that the people living here are God-fearing Muslims who have always shunned the evils of gambling and alcohol.'

Mrs Sadiq gasped in wonder, but her mother could stand no more. Muttering Persian expletives under her breath she stood up and made to leave the room. The Baba, noticing the movement through half-open eyes, called after her.

'The spirits do not like the colour of your hair,' he chastised her, pointing at her shock of scarlet hair. Mrs Sadiq bundled her mother from the room before she could do the Baba some harm.

'You are all naked to me,' he continued. 'I see your bodies, and I see your thoughts.' The ladies shuffled uneasily, adjusting their saris and dupatas, and closing their legs together tightly. 'Is there anyone in this room who would now like to seek my advice?'

Mrs Sadiq stepped forward eagerly, and kissing his hand asked that the Baba pray for the health and wealth of her family.

'Bring me a jug of water,' he demanded.

A pitcher of water was hurriedly fetched by Laxmi and placed before the holy man. Holding the Qur'ān in his left hand and the feather duster in his right, he and his devotees chanted strange verses for a minute and a half. Then, putting his accoutrements down, he took the pitcher in his hands and blew into it, depositing a mouthful of saliva in the water.

'Drink a teaspoon of this water each day and your family will never know misery.' With these words he presented an ornamental silver box with a slit just wide enough to accommodate the gratitude of the faithful. Mrs Sadiq produced a 200 rupee note which she gratefully thrust into the container, and then instructed Laxmi to put the pitcher in the refrigerator. A steady stream of the newly converted then filed forward to buy Baba's beneficence, and when the sitting was concluded the Baba held Mrs Sadiq's head in his hands and blew on her hair. She sighed happily as Baba Jin and his entourage returned to their car in the driveway.

'Mama, I feel cleansed,' she told her mother when she returned to the house. 'Baba chanted something from the Qur'ān and blew on my hair.'

'Then I should wash it thoroughly if I were you,' Mrs Shirazi observed.

A week after the visit of Baba Jin, when young Zeebande accidentally knocked a tumbler of water to the floor, Mrs Sadiq begged mercy from the spirits and was about to strike the child when Mrs Shirazi prevented her.

'Papool, you do not seriously believe that I would allow any of you to drink water that a charlatan had spat in, do you? When Laxmi brought the pitcher into the kitchen last week I immediately threw the water down the sink, cleaned the pitcher, and then replaced it with clean, boiled water. Zeebande has not spilled your precious water. I did.'

At this point Dr Sadiq walked into the kitchen.

'Thirsty work this gardening, Abaji,' he said to his mother-in-law. 'Do you think you might let me have some of that water from the fridge.' He smiled mischievously at his wife and then left the room.

'Infidel,' she called after him.

Dr Sadiq and the Spinach

Dr Sadiq picked at his spinach, evidently not enjoying it. 'Regular as clockwork,' Sharif had always announced ritually each evening as he placed the plate of lightly boiled spinach before the doctor. A touch of salt, a dash of pepper, and a small bowl of yoghurt – the doctor hadn't altered his hors-d'oeuvre in fifteen years. But Sharif was in Guranwalla, his mother taken ill, and he had sent his cousin Amir to the Sadiq household as a locum for three weeks. Amir was not as conversant as his cousin with the doctor's delicate palate, however, and though the rest of the household had noticed no discernible difference in the food, the doctor certainly had.

'What's the matter, Sadiq?' his wife snapped. 'You've hardly eaten two mouthfuls this past week. Where's your appetite gone? You'll waste away, mark my words. It's those cold showers you insist on taking every day. A cold shower never gave anyone an appetite.'

That seemed something of a non sequitur to the doctor, but he nodded agreement anyway.

'I think cook has been putting a little chilli and cumin in the spinach,' he observed. 'I suppose he means well, and after all he's only with us for two more weeks.'

'Are you a man or a mouse?' his wife exploded. 'We're not running a charity here. We pay these people to cook food as we like it, not how they like it. If he isn't preparing your food correctly he needs to be told. And just for once you can tell him yourself. I'm tired of the servants thinking that I'm a bad-tempered ogre while they see you as some kind of angel. Get in that kitchen and lay down the law.'

The doctor reluctantly rose from his seat.

'And Sadiq!' his wife called after him. 'No pussyfeet!'

The cook stiffened obediently as his master entered the kitchen.

'Mr Rehman, I wonder if I might have a word with you,' he said in his most immaculate Urdu, addressing the servant with the honorific third person, his gentle voice not rising much above pianissimo. 'Do you think, my dear man, if it's not too much trouble, you could dispense with the chilli in my spinach. Don't get me wrong, Mr Rehman, your food is delicious and I would not dream of suggesting otherwise. Far from it, you are a first-class cook and we all agree that your food has been of the highest quality. Even little Zeebande is eating twice as much these days. But you see, sir, I have a very delicate stomach, through no fault of your own of course, and as a result of living in England for so many years I am not used to the spices that you use. I realise that you weren't to know this and it is entirely my fault for not telling –'

'Sadiq!' his wife interrupted. 'Are you trying to make love to the man?'

Unbeknown to the doctor she had followed him to the kitchen and heard the whole conversation.

'Cook, the doctor likes his spinach lightly boiled with a touch of salt. No chillies! No cumin! Just boiled! Have you got that? If you can't cook, get out of the kitchen. There's plenty that can.'

The cook nodded obediently and Dr Sadiq returned to the dining-room wishing that he had just eaten the food. His wife followed him back to the table.

'You don't understand English, Sadiq? No pussyfeet I said. No pussyfeet!'

Nasir and Taj

Nasir and Taj live in a village in the Punjab. Their hair is in a simple plait with a parting in the middle. They know the Qur'ān by heart in Arabic, but do not know its meaning. They are married, have several children, and for the past twenty years have worked the land. Once they danced the twist in a grand house in Bahadurabad.

'Who are you?' I demanded to know. 'Do you want your hair cut?'

Nasir and Taj had moved to Sind from the Punjab following the death of their mother. Their father, Nazeer, was a farmer who had sought work that could keep him close to them and had taken the job as cook at a house down the street and had arrived with his two children the previous day. They appeared a strange pair, Nasir and Taj, their dark brown shalwar qamizes hanging slackly from undernourished bodies, dupatas wrapped modestly around their heads. But they smiled at me, and agreed to have their hair cut.

It was of course a disaster – after all I was not yet ten – and when Nasir, only two days in Bahadurabad, felt the bare nape of her neck with her hand she went into convulsions of sobbing. Even some of my best clothes and my new bangles could not stop her and that evening, when she and her sister came round to see me, she told me that her father had been very cross. He was a strict Muslim and believed that young girls with long hair should always have a parting in the middle with a single plait.

Though still a child this was a strange notion to me: my own relaxed up-bringing had not prepared me for it. In my family the women had always made the rules and it seemed absurd to me that a man should decide the hair-style of his daughter. I therefore went with Nasir to see her father and explain to him that it was I who was to blame, that it was I who had cut his daughter's hair.

Nazeer was watering his employer's garden as we entered the gate. He looked up at us both and smiled with his green Punjabi eyes and calm friendly face. My anger melted instantly. It was all I could do to ask him apologetically why he was so strict about something as irrelevant as the parting in his daughter's hair.

'We are simple people, and fashion is not for us,' he told me. 'We try to lead our lives by the teachings of Mohammed, may peace be upon him, and he has taught us to respect our wives, our mothers, and our daughters. I have to protect my two daughters in order that they don't forget their role as women in our religion and culture.'

Nazeer was so calm and temperate that it was difficult to judge whether he was telling me off or apologising. But I knew I liked him, and that he had just given me the first lesson in accepting that not everyone who disagreed with me was necessarily bad. He never interfered in my friendship with Nasir and Taj, and would accept the clothes and bangles that I gave his daughters without embarrassment, always careful to make sure that he cooked me some little niblet in return. And provided that his daughters studied the Qur'ān each day it never concerned him that they should dance the twist to my sister's records, or that they should know the words of 'Saturday Night at the Movies' just as well as those of Mohammed. For two years I was inseparable from my two little friends and by the time that they left me they were able to speak immaculate English.

It was almost two years to the day after their arrival in the street that Nazeer received a letter from his village in the Punjab. His only brother had suffered a heart attack and there was no one to attend to their ancestral plot of land. His brother was too poor to hire workers, and his children would starve unless someone could be found to work the land. Nazeer was therefore obligated by blood to return to his village and take responsibility for the land. In any case, it would make more economic sense if the whole family lived under one roof.

I was distraught. I felt that I was losing my own children. I begged my grandmother to adopt them, but of course it couldn't be done. The day they were to leave, however, I was given the morning off school. I waited by the gates as they appeared from the house with their small tin trunks. We never got to speak. We just cried in each other's arms for ten minutes while their father fetched a taxi to take them to the train station. The last I saw of them was two small faces peering from the back window as the taxi turned the corner at the top of the street.

The Accident

The briefcase clattered to the ground as the swerving vehicle failed to avoid the unfortunate pedestrian. The car came to a halt some twenty yards from the crumpled figure and the shaken driver ran back to inspect the damage.

Dr Sadiq had witnessed the whole incident from the lounge window of 63 Talgarth Road, yet it had not appeared to register. In truth his thoughts were elsewhere, elsewhere with the daughter he had left behind four thousand miles away in Pakistan. He had just spoken to her on the phone and she and her mother had been sheltering under the dining table during an air-raid. The child had been excited, too young to know danger, but Dr Sadiq cursed his helplessness. He had no stomach for war, especially a war between his adopted country and the country of his birth, and he had pleaded with his wife to allow him to take Zeebande with him on his trip to England. It was some time since he had seen his son Yusuf, and the outbreak of hostilities had afforded him the perfect opportunity to leave Pakistan for a while. It was doubtful if his heart would have endured the stress of the air-raids, even if he had dodged the bombs.

'If we die, we die together,' his wife had told him. And for once he had not been able to rely on the support of his mother-in-law. She had been at one with her daughter in refusing to allow the child out of their sight. He had therefore reluctantly travelled alone.

'What's all the commotion?' Helen asked him. His

daughter-in-law had been preparing dinner and had been drawn from the kitchen by the noise outside.

'Oh, there appears to have been an accident,' the doctor remarked absent-mindedly, shaken from his contemplation.

Wiping her hands dry with a tea-towel, Helen looked over his shoulder, just in time to see the driver of the car shouting to a passer-by to call an ambulance.

'Doctor,' she cried, seeing the crumpled form on the road outside. 'What on earth are you thinking of just standing there watching? Someone's been injured. Go and see if you can help, for goodness sake.'

The doctor suddenly woke from his reverie.

'Oh yes, I suppose I ought to. I'm sorry. I was miles away.'

By the time he had gathered himself and reached the scene of the accident a small crowd had gathered, all murmuring concern, but all doing little about it.

'Let us through,' Helen urged the crowd. 'This gentleman is a doctor. Move aside, please.'

Hitching his right trouser-leg up a touch the doctor bent down on one knee, genuflecting to the injured man. With deliberate and commendable thoroughness he loosened the gentleman's tie, undid the top button, and checked limbs one by one for broken bones. After a few minutes, having established that there was no serious injury, he eased himself up and adjusted his trousers.

'There seems to be no damage done,' he advised his daughter-in-law and the gathered throng. 'He's just a little shocked. I wonder if you could fetch a glass of brandy, please, Helen? If there's none in the cabinet you'll find a bottle in my bedroom.'

Helen hurried anxiously into the house and returned a few moments later with a generous glass of Rémy Martin. The doctor took off his jacket, folded it neatly, and then placed it under the head of the shaken pedestrian. Standing up he took the glass from his daughter-in-law's hand, nodded assurance to the crowd, and in one gulp downed the brandy.

'Ah, that's much better. Now we'll just wait for the ambulance.'

The Egg Ritual

Dr Sadiq was not well, considerably weakened by a second heart attack. He sensed that he did not have long left. He rested now in the afternoon heat, eyes shut, lying on the bed in his white shalwar qamiz, breathing in the scents from the garden through the open window.

Elsewhere in the house Zeebande was looking for coal. She already had an egg and bowl, and wanted to cast off the evil eye. Her father heard her enter the room but kept his eyes closed. She crept to his bedside so as not to wake him and placed the bowl on the floor.

'Hello, bibi,' he said, opening his eyes and smiling his toothless smile. He had lost his teeth in a car accident many years earlier and his dentures lay in a glass of disinfected water by the bedside. 'Can't you sleep?'

'I've come to ward off the evil eye of jealous people so that you get better soon,' she told him. Her grandmother had performed the ritual on her many times when she had been younger.

The doctor pulled himself up from his repose and turned towards his daughter.

'Go ahead, bibi,' he encouraged her.

She took the egg from the bowl, and with the charcoal that she had found in the courtyard chalked a circle of a quarter of an inch in diameter on the egg-shell. Then pressing the egg carefully against her father's forehead she made a mark with the charcoal. She then described a circle around his head with the egg before breaking it in the bowl at his feet, all the while chanting some Qur'ānic verse that her grandmother had taught her.

'No one will hurt you now,' she assured him before

running from the room. She did not wish her mother to find her showing her father too much affection. Her love had to be strictly rationed.

Dr Sadiq rose from his bed and looked over his garden from the window, watching his daughter run into the street to find her friends. He was sad, for he knew that he would not live to see her marry.

A Doctor Dies

They wouldn't let me see my father, Clause 43b of the Hospital Administration Ordinance 1949, no child under the age of sixteen years shall be allowed into the hospital grounds after the hour of 1900, not even if your father is ill, or dying even, not even if you never see your father again, which I didn't, not alive, only in the drawer with cotton wool in his ears and nostrils, the same Seventh Day Hospital where I was born. Bring her quickly I want to see my child, but we arrived too late – it was after seven, no I'm sorry, madam, it's against the rules, yes I know he's a doctor but rules are rules, no I must insist it's more than my job's worth, well just this once but only in the garden, she can see from there, and only five minutes you must understand that this is a special favour. See there he is, Zeeba, my mother said, that window over there, and then I saw him just below the sky, so high up, but I saw him smile and I saw him wave and I wonder if there was a tear in his eye for he knew that it was the last time, and if I had known he needn't have waved, for rules or no rules I would have been with him up there in his arms.

Mother looked pale when we got home. Have something to eat Nani said to her, no I'll just have a cup of tea, but Nani made her egg on toast anyway, it'll do you good, you have to eat, but why was my mother so pale, why did she look so frightened, and why hadn't I been sent to bed, they never let me stay up so late. And then my mother whispered, whispered to Nani so I couldn't hear, but I did, he gave me his watch and his glasses and his teeth to bring home and he's told the ward-boy to cancel the newspaper, you know how much he likes his newspaper, so why would he do that and how will he see without his glasses? I won't be needing them tomorrow he said. Oh they'll be discharging him in the morning that's why, my grandmother had said, just you see, but we'll have to make sure that he stops working so hard, no more trips to treat the poor, no more trips to Burmah Shell, no more trips to the airport, we can clear the storeroom and he can have his clinic there so that we can keep an eye on him, everything'll be just fine. Appai seemed a little better and I went to bed reassured, but oh what a dreadful morning, Nani by my bedside stroking my hair, tears rolling down her face and the sound of wailing women in the living-room. What's that noise I said, I want to see my mother, yes of course but why don't you change into your nice black dress first, so I did, and in the lounge I saw black, only black. What's going on I asked my grandmother, gripping tighter, who are all these people, though I recognised some, they were moaning and they were groaning and they were beginning to upset me but then they went quiet when they saw me, and only one didn't stop, a quiet sobbing in the corner of the room, it was Appai. I should have known she said, why else would he give me his watch and glasses, why else would he cancel his newspaper, I should have known. I broke free from Nani and ran to my mother and she sobbed some more, is Daddy very ill I asked, she put her arms around me, no, Daddy has gone to heaven, and the wailing began again but louder this time, why are they all crying, what is wrong with them, for I didn't understand death and Daddy could never die.

The driver is here, I heard someone call, I grabbed my mother's hand, where are you going, just to sign some papers, what papers, I'm coming with you; it's just your father's discharge from hospital, Nani said; is he coming home, I said. There was more wailing and they tried to pull me away from my mother, my daughter is coming with me she said, I sat between Appai and Fairy Auntie in the car and looked through the window but nothing seemed real. My mother was telling Fairy Auntie that she had had it all planned, a clinic in the house so that they could keep an eye on him and then about midnight the phone had rung, don't worry Mrs Sadiq it was a very peaceful death, just three hiccups and he was gone.

At the hospital they wanted me to wait outside but I insisted for it wasn't seven o'clock, we didn't go through the entrance door we went through the exit, and I saw so many people, all crying, there were relatives, there were friends, there were his patients, there were jockeys, there were trainers, what on earth are they all doing here I thought and we fought our way through them, and there was a man in a white coat with a paper and a pen. He opened a drawer and there was my father with cotton wool in his ears and his nose, you're trying to murder him I screamed, take that wool out he can't breathe, and there was a traffic jam outside a fruit-stall on the way to the graveyard and the radio was playing ever so loud, and they wouldn't let me near the grave, it took four aunties to hold me back but I still broke free and they couldn't catch me. I cried to the mullah to let my father go, don't kill him, don't bury him alive, but they did, and the fire wasn't lit for three days, no food was cooked as is the tradition, on the first day it was sent by Rakshanda's in-laws, and the second day by Mr Shirazi, a friend of the family, and the third day by Nusrat Bhutto. And then I played with knives in my bedroom and I played with Daddy's heart tablets but they did me no harm, and then eventually when they knew that I was OK they took me to his clinic because I wanted to go. I felt in the drawer, the one to his desk, and I found five photographs, one of his wife, one of his first wife, one of his daughter, and one each of his sons, the doctor and his families.

Bun-Kebabs

'Bun-kebabs for little lady, no charge,' Ali declared in his thick Punjabi accent. My father had attended his wife when she had developed difficulties during the birth of their second child and he knew that I spoke English.

Ali's kebab stall nestled among the drooping neem trees by the Keyam cinema in Sindi Muslim Housing Society. It had been ingeniously adapted from a discarded four-poster bed; he had replaced the mattress with several strips of sheet metal, and had draped a piece of black tarpaulin over the four supports to keep the sun from the food. Bicycle wheels had been welded to the four legs for ease of transport. The stall stood directly below the watchful gaze of Waheed Murad, who was a permanent presence on the film hoardings above the cinema entrance. Ali was kept company most days by Sabir, who sold the best paans in Karachi.

Following my father's death our family had moved from Bahadurabad to a smaller house in Sindi Muslim Cooperative Housing Society. I had quickly made friends with two sisters, Saju and Anisa, and it was they who had first taken me to the Keyam cinema. Saju was the younger, small with buck-teeth; Anisa was tall, a tomboy with fair hair and a hooked nose. Both shared my adolescent proclivity for the dirt and grease of the street hawkers and in Ali we found the embodiment of all that was delicious.

Ali's skin was darkened by many years exposed to the sun. His one white shirt was yellowed by turmeric and grease and his flared khaki trousers were always rolled up a couple of folds to reveal two brown pins of legs fitted into dusty tan sandals. A gas stove burned below the greased iron plate, black with use, and flies hovered around the glass chutney jar covered with a faded piece of muslin cloth. Invariably unshaven, and with long blackened fingernails, Ali would scoop the kebab from the plate with his spatula and in the same movement roll it into delicious, freshly cooked bread. A liberal splash of tomato and onion chutney with his wooden spoon, and the equation would be complete. It was a feast of smells: the stale odour of gas from the ancient stove, the pungent burning chillies, the ecstasy of cooking bread, and always the joss-sticks burning slowly at the side of the stall.

This was real food, the food given to me so selflessly by our servants and by the parents of the poor children who used to keep me company outside the Gymkhana Club, eager to make some offering to Doctor Sahib's daughter, Doctor Sahib who had always treated them without charge.

No trip to the bun-kebab-wallah was complete, however, without one of Sabir's 'yum-yum' paans. The leaf laid flat in his left hand, a pinch of aniseed with his right, some sweet supari, some grated coconut, a little cardamon, and then a lick of honey to seal the paan. And occasionally, just very occasionally, we would treat ourselves to one of his specials – the 'sweetheart' paans at five rupees, and the 'wedding-night' paans at ten rupees. They were rumoured to possess aphrodisiac qualities and each contained Sabir's 'magic ingredient'. They were twice the size of the normal paans, one wrapped in silver paper and the other in gold. Saju, Anisa, and I were of course too young to test the validity of the rumour, but they certainly had a strange effect on us as we wandered back through the warren of alleyways in Sindi Muslim Society, and we were always more amused than scared after a 'wedding-night' paan when on our way home we passed the Karachi pederasts parading their members on the waste ground between Allam Iqbal Street and Sufi Street.

'Bun-kebab for little lady, no charge.'

Ali is no longer at his stall outside the Keyam cinema, though I am told that he is still alive. Sabir recognised me immediately though.

' "Wedding-night" paan?' he smiled. He took the leaf, added aniseed, supari, coconut, and cardamom, and then I watched in horror as he reached for his magic ingredient and proceeded to crumble a full quarter-ounce of hashish into the paan.

Varsy Uncle

The first time I met Varsy Uncle he gave me 200 rupees Eid money. He was mad as a hatter but I loved him anyway, for his crazed tales of demons, jinn, and witchcraft always made perfect sense to me. They say that things might have been different though, had not Bengaloosh cast a spell on him.

As unprepossessing a man as you were likely to meet, Maqbool Varsy was average in many ways. Of average height, average build, and even average weight, his singular most striking feature was his startled, protruding eyes, eyes of the geckos that were later to keep him company in the empty servants' quarters. Born into a family of Delhi traders it was agreed that Varsy had done very well for himself. Through a combination of industry and determination he had dragged himself from the gutter and had managed to establish for himself a thriving import-export business. His work took him all around the world, staying in the best hotels and always tipping the staff heavily. How this poor Delhi boy glowed with pride the time that the Geneva Hilton doorman feigned recognition from an earlier stay.

'Take this, my man,' he had crowed, ostentatiously pressing a large-denomination note into the doorman's hand. 'There's plenty more where that came from.'

Dear Varsy Uncle. How they must have hated him!

It was during this period of prosperity, on one of his regular trips to Dacca, that he first met Bengaloosh. Bengaloosh worked the bars of the best hotels and earned for herself a considerable income. Varsy's lack of sophistication made him easy prey for this beautiful Bangladeshi siren, and his business trips to Dacca began to increase at commensurate pace to his love for the woman. His distraught wife, by now well aware of her husband's fixation, bore her trials with dignity. That is, until Varsy announced his intention to marry Bengaloosh. Then, something had to be done.

It was Iqbal Chowdhury who first suggested that Bengaloosh had perhaps cast a spell on Varsy Uncle. The whole world knows of the Bengal witches, he had said, and there could be no other explanation. Iqbal Chowdhury had been with the Varsys for many years and was indeed an excellent cook. Nicknamed Molana for his long red beard and his deep religious beliefs, he had the bearing and the gait of a military man. The hapless Mrs Varsy was quick to seize on the suggestion and therefore petitioned the help of Bibi June in dispelling the mischievous spirits. Varsy himself wondered if there might be some truth in it, and torn between his deep respect for his wife and his love for Bengaloosh, he took to whisky and Mogadons to quell his internal torment. Seeing Varsy Auntie's deep unhappiness and her concern for her husband, Iqbal Chowdhury kindly offered to intercede with Allah on Varsy's behalf. But the spirits of Johnny Walker and the magic potions of Bibi June proved too strong an adversary for a man of his simple faith and it was not too long before Varsy plunged into the abyss of delirium. His psychosis reached its peak during the conflict of 1971, and when he decided to have his own house bombed Iqbal Chowdhury fled, fearing for his own sanity and life.

Iqbal Chowdhury's replacement was cast from an entirely different mould. Abdul Hassan was nervous and edgy, and his youthful appearance and sprightly step belied his fifty years. Arriving at the Varsys at the height of the conflict he took a daily interest in the war reports, and was eager that everyone should know that were it not for his bad back he would most certainly have volunteered for duty.

'A true patriot I am, sir, a true patriot,' he used to tell Varsy Uncle, not realising that Varsy neither knew nor cared who he was.

When the air-raids started in 1971 our family had been invited to stay with the Varsys. They had a huge house with a labyrinth of secret passageways and cellars and it was considered that we would be safer there.

'In-laws are family,' the newly confident Masroor had proclaimed when he had visited us with his young bride and child. 'My house is your house,' he had declared, having assumed the mantle of head of household as a consequence of his father's insanity. Besides, my mother and Varsy Auntie were firm friends by now. And so it was that when the sirens sounded our two families would file down the cellar steps with gas lanterns to light our way. Each household had received strict instructions that all lights were to be extinguished at the first sound of the siren. Masroor always led the way, with my sister and young nephew following close behind. I would follow with Varsy Auntie, and then my mother, my grandmother, and Laxmi would bring up the rear. Varsy Uncle would never join us, preferring the company of his invisible friends in the kitchen. The cook sheltered in his own quarters at the rear of the building.

Varsy Uncle never sought to explain why he decided to invite the Indians to bomb his own house but instinct had made Masroor climb the cellar steps one day and return to the upper building to check that all the lights were out. He was mortified to find his father wandering among the rooms turning the lights back on. Using perhaps a little more force than was absolutely necessary he bundled his father down into the cellar and then returned to the house to plunge it into darkness once more. From that day, he took the further precaution of disconnecting the fuse-box during the raids. But his father, still refusing to join his family in the cellar, was further down the road of insanity than Masroor had imagined, and it was the new cook, Abdul Hassan, who first heard Varsy Uncle screaming at the skies during one of the air-raids. Peering nervously from his quarters he had made out his master in the centre of the garden, shining a pocket torch to the skies, and imploring the gods, 'Bomb here, bomb here!'

It is likely that Varsy Uncle and I were the only ones in the household who were not aware at the time that the jets roaring overhead were our own brave fighters, scrambled from the nearby airport to intercept the incoming raiding party, for the Indian planes could not possibly have approached from that direction. But no matter! Varsy Uncle wanted his house bombed.

Into the fourth week of the air-raids we had settled into a routine. The sirens always sounded at night at a time when we would normally have eaten, and so after our sojourn in the cellar we would return to the house when we heard the all-clear and the cook would prepare food a little later than usual. Never knowing how long we would be below ground the ladies had decided that there was no sense in cooking earlier. Varsy Uncle by this time was left to his own resources, Masroor not sharing his father's optimism that the pilots would be able to see the light of his small torch. He saw no sense in spoiling his fun.

It was on one particular evening that following the all-clear we had looked forward to our meal with some relish as the blackout had lasted longer than usual. But, unable to find the cook, Masroor was becoming increasingly agitated and therefore the ladies decided to prepare the food themselves. Though the cook often left the house to buy Khamiri bread from the pathans in Rizwan

Colony, he was rarely away for longer than a half-hour. On this particular occasion however he had been gone a full hour when there was a sharp rapping on the door. Raised voices could be heard as Masroor answered and, my curiosity excited, I rushed to the hallway to watch the activity. I was just in time to see Masroor brushed aside as three officers of the Military Intelligence, five uniformed policemen, and a cook, all marched into the house in single file, and through into the lounge.

'Where is the spy?' they demanded.

Varsy Uncle was quickly identified by the cook and manhandled into the kitchen. Three of the officers stood guard over him as the other five followed Abdul Hassan into the garden. Armed with their own powerful torches they conducted a thorough search of the garden which lasted some twenty minutes. Then, returning to the kitchen, one of the policemen was ordered to stand guard in the hallway and the door was closed behind him. Dressed in smart green khakis he stood beside the kitchen door, impervious to Masroor's pleas. The adults in the lounge whispered in concerned tones, while my nephew and I found the whole affair terribly exciting. Voices could be heard from the kitchen, and it appeared that Varsy Uncle was doing the bulk of the talking. It was half an hour before the kitchen door was heard to open and we all rushed into the hallway. The commander at their head, the officers emerged from the kitchen, one by one, and filed past us in stunned silence, towards the main door and out into the street. The cook was the last to emerge, and pausing briefly before us, he followed the others into the street, never to be seen at the house again. Varsy Uncle was still talking in the kitchen, not apparently aware that the officers had left. And then, suddenly seeing the concerned household descending upon him, he quickly retrieved his torch from the table, gave me a conspiratorial wink, and headed for the garden as the evening flight to Singapore could be heard taking off from the nearby airport.

Baqar Uncle

We are undoubtedly a less squeamish people than our European peer group; death is that much more familiar to us. For my own part, by the time I was ten years old I had lived through two wars, lost my father, and witnessed on a daily basis the brutality of life for the street people of Karachi. However, nothing could have quite prepared me for the story of Baqar Uncle and the day he first met his wife.

Baqar Uncle was 6 foot 7 inches and boasted the proportions of a bear. Even without his awesome physique Baqar would still have induced fear in the bravest of men, not least because of the sinister scar that ran from his left eye to the lobe of his left ear. Like a great many Lucknowis he spoke beautiful Urdu, had immaculate manners, but hated Sunnis. He was a relative of my father's – the accepted wisdom suggested that he was my second cousin – and spoke to me as to a younger sister rather than the child that I was. I was just six years old when he first told me the story, sweeping me up in his arms and carrying me piggy-back from the garden where I had been tormenting my pet dog.

'. . . and there was blood everywhere,' he assured me, warming to his theme, and startling my grandmother who was reading her newspaper in the cool of the lounge.

She looked up protectively as Baqar threw me playfully on to the sofa and parked his own huge presence beside me.

'At that time there were regular communal riots in

Lucknow, the Sunnis always trying to cause trouble for us Shias. I was a Shia youth leader back then, proud of it too, and I wasn't going to take any nonsense from those blood-sucking bastards.'

'Baqar!' my grandmother interrupted sharply. 'Language!'

Baqar muttered an apology and continued with his story.

'We had been fighting all afternoon. It had begun when the Sunnis started hurling stones and bricks at our procession during the month of mourning. The procession scattered and a pitched battle broke out. Many people were killed that day, and I myself was badly injured, stab wounds to my stomach and left arm. But my faith in Hussain kept me going, and I managed to struggle away from the battle in order to get my wounds tended to. I was in a back street, leaning against the wall of a building, sensing that I was about to faint. I closed my eyes for a moment, and when I opened them again I was confronted by two men with knives, and in front of them the Sunni maulvi who had orchestrated all the trouble. He started screaming at me, insulting our faith, calling us child abusers, all kinds of names. I can still see him now. He had dyed red hair and a ridiculous beard that hadn't quite grown. His teeth were rotten and I could smell his foul breath as he ranted at me. 'Die, infidel, die,' he was shouting as his two sidekicks advanced on me. I prayed to Ali for strength and drew the machete that I had hidden beneath my qamiz.'

I was wide-eyed as Baqar extended his right arm above his head, his left outstretched in front of him, and with a powerful sweep crashed the side of his right hand into the palm of his left.

'Whoosh! Off came his head, rolling into the gutter among the sewage and rotting vegetables.' He picked an apple from the bowl on the coffee table in front of him and rolled it across the room. I felt sick.

'Baqar!' my grandmother barked again, putting her newspaper down. 'She's only a child. Have you no sense at all?'

Baqar hung his head at this fresh rebuke and then reached forward to pick up the apple. He tossed it back into the bowl and looked at me to see if he should continue.

'His two sidekicks dropped their weapons and fled down the street.' He was speaking softly now. 'I kicked the body into the gutter and then staggered after them. But they were too fast for me. My earlier effort had drained me of all my energy. I remember people staring at me as I pushed my way through the crowds. I was losing blood fast. I must have passed out, for the next thing I remember was opening my eyes and seeing the most beautiful woman in the world, Catherine, the woman who was later to become my wife, the woman to whom I owe everything.'

He smiled.

'She was a Christian, the daughter of a vicar. She had returned from cleaning his church that afternoon to find me sleeping in her father's armchair. Her father had apparently returned from visiting his parishioners that day and had noticed a trail of blood down the street. He was alarmed to find that it led into his own back yard and following the trail he eventually found me lying there half-conscious. To this day I don't know how I got there, but perhaps it was in my kismet, for the vicar tended my wounds and gave me food and drink to help me recover my strength. His daughter was only sixteen, but she looked after me for a whole week as though I were her own blood. She captured my heart, and it was with a feeling of deep shame that I left the home of these two saintly people a week later. I felt ashamed that I couldn't repay their kindness, and ashamed that I had fallen for a Christian girl. After all, I had just killed for my own faith, but was now captivated by someone from another.'

He shook his head in mild self-rebuke.

'But love is stronger than faith, Zeeba,' he continued, 'and two days later I returned to ask for her hand in marriage. And look at her now,' he stated proudly. 'She is more of a Muslim than I could ever hope to be; my beautiful wife Zainab.'

Nani had picked up her newspaper again, happy that Baqar had learnt his lesson. He looked over at her, mischief in his eyes. He winked at me and put a finger to his lips. He reached towards the fruit bowl.

'Whoosh! Off came his head,' he thundered, rolling the apple directly at Nani's feet.

The Diagnosis (2)

My grandmother is as sharp as a razor. She has travelled the globe, and boasts many influential friends. She has bought and sold land, dabbled in import-export, and to this day keeps herself busy repackaging old packs of cards to earn a little spending money. She is pious, and though I fail to share her conviction that prayers five times a day will secure Allah's protection for me in my dotage, I admire her faith. It is a source of endless wonder to me, therefore, how such a woman can believe in ghosts.

By all accounts I was very ill. I don't remember it myself and so have to rely on what my grandmother tells me. All the events of that year remain a hazy grey. It was the year of my father's death, and I had apparently returned home from school as normal one day. Some time during dinner I had complained of a burning sensation in my stomach, and later that evening I had developed a temperature. My mother, by then imagining herself to be something of an apothecary, had given me antibiotics from my father's old medicine cabinet. My grandmother had been appalled at her arrogance and demanded that a doctor be called.

'The girl needs a doctor, not your damnfool guesses,' she had told my mother. 'My husband was an army captain but I never imagined that I could march his troops into battle.'

My mother fumed, but had nonetheless called a doctor when I became delirious at about midnight. I was injected with who-knows-what by Dr Khoja, and he confided to Appai and Nani that I was not well, that he was prescribing a strong medicine, and that my condition would have to be monitored closely. He lent them the encouragement that if my temperature did not subside in a day or two they might lose me. This news sent my grandmother scurrying for her prayer-mat and my mother sacrificed a lamb to distribute to the poor. But Allah ignored their offerings and Dr Khoja's medicine offered me no respite.

By day four my temperature had reached a frightening 104 degrees and on the recommendation of Mrs Varsy a Dr Kaiser was called. He had just returned from London with fresh qualifications and had a growing reputation in Karachi.

'The girl needs to be in hospital,' he opined.

'Never!' my mother answered him. 'That is where people go to die. Bring anything she needs to this house. Money is no problem.'

Dr Kaiser deferred to her demands and a glucose drip was set up and penicillin injected. My mother and Nani organised a rota system to watch over me, Nani volunteering for the first shift. When my mother came to relieve her at three in the morning, however, she refused to budge and so my mother gladly returned to bed.

Nani awoke with a start in the morning when my mother entered the room. Fatigue and worry had taken their toll, for I wasn't getting any better. She rose from her chair and with the certainty of a fanatic announced to my mother that she was taking me off my medicine.

'Are you mad? What gives you the right to make such a decision?'

'I have been by the child's side since the moment that she was born. That's what gives me the right!'

'And what's that supposed to mean?'

'It isn't supposed to mean anything. It is simply a fact.'

'And I suppose the fact that I carried her for nine months counts for nothing?'

'Eight months and two weeks. She was premature.'

My mother erupted at Nani's impertinence.

'Are you trying to tell me that you love her more than I do, my own daughter? A mother is a mother,' she blustered.

'I am taking the child off her medicine,' Nani continued as though the conversation with her daughter hadn't taken place. Appai threw the tea that she had brought for Nani on to the floor and stormed from the room.

'I'm glad you understand,' Nani called after her. 'She's really a little pussy in my hands,' she congratulated herself.

On the evening of the fifth day I awoke feeling unwell, but no longer feverish. My grandmother brought me some coffee and when my mother returned from her errands called her into the room.

'Your daughter's asking for you,' she explained.

'Zeeba! My heart, my liver, my child,' Appai gushed, embracing me. 'The penicillin must have taken effect at last.'

'Dr Sadiq cured her,' my grandmother corrected her.

'Your nani should get some sleep,' my mother whispered to me. 'She's talking gibberish.'

'Dr Sadiq cured his daughter,' my grandmother reaffirmed. 'I called on the spirits of our family last night and Dr Sadiq was the only one to answer. He came to the room and sat with us. He stroked his daughter's hair and sang to her. "Don't listen to these donkeys," he told me. "Stop all the medicine, Abaji," he said. "These clowns Khoja and Kaiser shouldn't be allowed near a hospital. The child has measles. Penicillin and antibiotics will simply suppress it. That's what's causing the fluctuating temperature. Give her nothing, and she will have measles by the evening." Dr Sadiq cured his daughter!'

'Did I ever tell you about the time that your father visited me in my sleep when you were ill?' my mother said to me recently.

Goodbye, Bahadurabad

'We need a house for twelve,' my mother demanded.

'Twelve!' my grandmother spluttered. 'There's only four of us.'

'Exactly!' my mother confirmed. 'Four of us, and an eight-man card-school. That makes twelve.'

'He has proved his case to the judge's satisfaction,' Baqi told us. 'The judge has ruled in the landlord's favour. He needs the house for his own family so you have just six months to find an alternative home. I'm sorry that I couldn't have been of more help.'

Baqi had fought the case on our behalf for more than a year. Shortly after my father's death we had been given notice by our landlord that he needed the house for his own use. We knew full well that he hoped to get a higher rent out of the new tenants, but we had been unable to convince the judge adjudicating on the matter. My father's death had left us with only a 690 rupee inheritance. He had seized his day in his old age, and we weren't now in a position to make our landlord an offer.

'Something will turn up,' my mother affirmed, and as a rule it did. 'Just so long as they look after Sadiq's garden. That's all I ask.'

Our specifications for a new home were quite explicit and a suitable alternative proved elusive. It had to be a house; a flat was out of the question. And it had to be detached and in a quiet area of the city away from the crowds. After all, we had to make a living, and the illegal card games were my mother's only source of income now. She was only too aware that three ageing women and a child would present easy prey for some witless fundamentalist wishing to ingratiate himself with the authorities, and she could not therefore run the risk of attracting attention to herself. Only a detached house would afford us the security needed for the late-night comings and goings of the card players. But such places were few and far between at a reasonable rent.

Something did turn up eventually, however. Mumtaz, an old friend of my mother's, arrived at the house one day with a young surveyor.

'This is Imtiaz Allam, Bhabi. He has been doing some work for me. He has a proposal to make you.'

The young man, no more than twenty-five years old, but with the bearing and manner of a fifty-year-old, shuffled awkwardly.

'Begum, I went to school with your daughter Rakshanda, and have always thought her to be the most beautiful girl in the world –'

'She is not for sale,' my mother interrupted, a little too rudely. 'She does not need a husband.'

My sister was by now divorced, and was staying with us for a short while in Karachi.

'No, no, no,' the surveyor quickly apologised. 'Don't get me wrong, Mrs Sadiq. I would never presume myself good enough for your daughter.'

My mother softened a little.

'No, it is simply that Mumtaz was telling me of your housing predicament when it occurred to me that I might have an answer, an answer to both our problems. You see, I have a four-bedroomed house in SMC Housing Society that my father left me on his death, and as I have no brothers or sisters it is far too big for me and my mother. We have managed to find a smaller place nearer to her friends where we would like to live but have unfortunately been unable to get a reasonable price for our own. I have only just taken it off the market. I was going to suggest that you move in as my tenants. Treat the house as your own. It would honour me that I could do something for Rakshanda's family, and it would also enable my mother and me to move to the little place that we have found.'

My mother nodded encouragingly.

'There's just one thing though,' he continued. 'The house needs a little work and I'm afraid I can't afford the repairs just yet.'

'Son, if I like the place you needn't worry about repairs. I shall pay for them myself,' she announced proudly. 'When can I see the place? We haven't long left and we'll need to arrange contracts.'

'Why not see it now?' he enquired. 'And surely we needn't worry about contracts. Rakshanda's mother is my mother,' he proclaimed a little absurdly, as this was the first time that he had seen Rakshanda or her mother in ten years. It was agreed, however, and Sultan was called to bring the car. Mumtaz and the young surveyor would lead the way and we would follow behind.

'I don't trust people who won't sign contracts,' Nani muttered to my mother, a little ungraciously.

'All you ever do is criticise,' my mother retorted. 'Contracts are for strangers. We are mother and son. Didn't you hear what he said?'

'How long did you say you've known him?' Nani observed icily, and marched to the waiting car.

In the late afternoon of 2 January 1974, the removal men loaded the last few pots and pans into the back of the van in the driveway. It was the first time that both the huge iron gates had been open together since the day that my family had first arrived there thirteen years earlier. We were leaving the next day.

I had been watching all the activity from the garden, tears streaming down my face. As long as we were at

38 Bahadurabad I had always felt that there was something of my father still with me, though he had been dead for over a year. But now I was being wrenched from my home.

I took in the scent of the double jasmine plants as I wandered the garden for a final time. I missed him more that night than I had ever done before, or have ever done since. I remembered the picked flowers he placed under my pillow at night and the smell of his Old Spice by my bed. I soaked in the fragrances as I moved among the flowers, picking a petal from each. I said goodbye to his trees, and embraced the fledgling guava that he had planted for me shortly before his death. I didn't stop crying until Laxmi led me through the gates the next morning for the last time.

The journey from Clifton took me twenty minutes. As I turned into Shaheed-e-Millat Road I could pick out the house quite easily. It was my father's birthday. He would have been eighty years old. I was strangely nervous and couldn't bring myself to drive straight to the gates so I parked by the house where Nasir and Taj had lived all those years ago and walked the rest of the way.

38 Bahadurabad looked lifeless and tired against the evening twilight. Paint was peeling from the walls, but it hadn't apparently been altered and the gates were still there, though not my father's name-plate. I rang the bell, but there was no answer. I imagined that I could smell jasmine and Old Spice and so pushed the gate. It wasn't locked. I stepped through, and then froze. I turned, banged the gate shut, and ran towards the car. The garden had been cemented and the trees chopped down.

Yusuf's Story

Daddy was a bigamist, or so someone told me last night. Daddy was a bigamist.

'Are you my brother?'

He was portly without appearing overweight, wiry grey hair on the retreat, and with an expensively cut suit that didn't quite fit the face. A pair of gold-framed spectacles rested on an ample nose and I noticed that one of the buttons of his white shirt had come undone. He looked nothing like my father. Indeed, had I not known that he was my brother I would most certainly have concluded that he was Jewish.

Looking at this amiable bookish figure smiling pleasantly in the doorway of the Belgravia apartment block I remembered that my grandfather had been an Iraqi, though I had never met him, and that this might account for the Semitic aspect of this agreeable fellow in front of me. But then I recalled that it was my mother's father, not my father's, who was the Iraqi, and that he had been a Persian, not an Arab. Perhaps he takes after his mother, I told myself as he stepped forward to take my hand.

'You must be Zeeba,' he announced, leading me into the hallway where he helped me from my jacket. 'Yusuf will be with you shortly. He's in a meeting at the moment and I'm to entertain you until he's finished. My name's Murray by the way. I'm Yusuf's accountant.'

I was almost disappointed. In the thirty seconds since the door had swung open I had reconciled myself to this likeable avuncular creature being my brother. I had imagined the tales that we were going to tell, the confidences that we were going to exchange, the memories that we were going to share. But his name was Murray, not Yusuf, and he was an accountant, not my brother.

'May I smoke?'

'Of course.'

'Thank you.'

'A drink?'

'Gin and tonic, please.'

We settled in a large office on the ground floor, a huge mahogany desk sitting imperiously in the centre of the room. Murray told me about his hip replacement operation as we waited, and I told him about my recent bout of pyelonephritis that had occasioned my isolation in Northwick Park Hospital, the symptoms bearing an unfortunate resemblance to typhoid. We were an unhealthy pair, Murray and I, and for half an hour we volleyed diseases and ailments across the room at each other until at four minutes past eight, I still remember the time, a tall dashing stranger swanned into the room. There was no mistaking my father's son this time.

'My God!' he greeted me. 'You look just like the old man.' He looked me over as we shook hands. 'I expected to see someone in a sari,' he quipped. 'How on earth did you track me down?'

Murray made a discreet exit and my brother led me to the lounge at the rear of the building. The decor was tastefully understated and the furniture quietly expensive. I was reeling from the shock of it all, seeing my father again, and I imagined that I might faint. He was taller and fairer than I had expected, in every way a European, but there was no mistaking my father in this elegant urbane stranger: Syed Mohamed Yusuf Sadiq, my father's youngest son, the brother I had never met.

It was approaching ten o'clock when he dropped his bombshell. We had exchanged curricula vitae, discussed our respective spouses, and even planned a trip to New

Orleans together. But, strangely, throughout the night my father occupied only a peripheral role in my brother's dialogue, a fact that at the time both surprised and worried me.

'It wasn't that I didn't want to meet you,' he was telling me. 'To be truthful, I wasn't really sure that you actually existed. Dad had told me about Zeeba, his daughter, but he was sixty years old at the time and I just assumed that he was talking about some waif and stray that he had "adopted" in the neighbourhood, perhaps a friend's or a neighbour's child. I couldn't really be expected to believe that a sixty-year-old with a dicky heart was still fathering children, could I? Besides, Dad and I weren't the best of friends by that time, not after what he did to my mother. You see, my mother was ill with cancer, and she hadn't got long to live. But Dad just upped and left, leaving us penniless in a tiny flat. The next thing I heard he had married again. My mother wasn't even dead and he had gone and got himself another wife . . .'

I couldn't sleep. My senses had taken a pounding and I was slightly drunk. I had expected to meet a new brother that night, not an iconoclast. I trawled my memory for some explanation, some counter to what Yusuf had told me. And then, just as sleep began to wash over me, I recalled a scene in my childhood, shortly after my father's death, when my mother and I had visited his surgery to collect his effects. I remembered the three photographs in a drawer, and a story that my mother told me as we sat together on his examining-couch.

Epilogue

'But who are they?' I insisted. 'I don't want to meet them.'

My mother took the photograph from my hand and studied it ruefully.

'They are your brothers, Zeeba. Jan and Yusuf. They were your father's children too. You remember Janny, don't you? He used to stay with us when you were little.'

I snatched the photograph from her hand again, but my mother was showing unaccustomed patience with me that morning and my bad manners went unpunished.

'But why would he never let me sit on his knee? Why wouldn't he play with me like Farid if he was my brother?'

I had recognised the smaller of the two boys immediately of course, but in an act of adolescent denial had convinced myself otherwise.

Janny had been a regular visitor to our home in my early childhood, I remembered being at his wedding. But I had never reconciled this filial bond with the detachment that he had always shown me. He had never been the brother that Farid was, had never shown any warmth towards me when my father and I had called in at his place on my way to school, and so I had forgotten that he was my brother at all and had not seen him for about five years, almost half my life.

My mother was pointing to the tall lady.

'That's Nora, your daddy's first wife. He was married to her a long time before he ever met me.'

I stared at her, unable to take my eyes from the hat. She was so poised and dignified.

'Jan and Yusuf were her children,' my mother continued. 'Your daddy's children. They were born in England when he used to live over there.'

'Why did I never see this boy?' I interrupted her, pointing to the taller but younger of the two.

'It's a long story, Zeeba,' she sighed. 'I'll tell you about it one day.'

'Tell me now!' I demanded.

My mother took a tissue from the sleeve of her qamiz and blew her nose, a gesture I recognised as one of reluctant forbearance. She slipped the tissue back in her sleeve and placed the photograph on the seat beside us.

'Your father was a kind sweet man, Zeeba. He never wilfully hurt anyone in his life.' She paused, considering her words. 'But he was irresponsible. He never grew up.' She shook her head at the memory of it all.

'I don't remember the year exactly, but it was at the time that your grandmother was married to Mohsin. Your grandmother had a friend, Tahir, a customs officer at the port, who used to call in the evenings for a game of cards. One day he asked your grandmother if she minded if he brought a friend of his along, a doctor who had just arrived from England with his family, and was staying with Tahir for a short while. That was when I first got to know your father, during those card games at Hamshat Villa, though I had in fact met him many years earlier at a party. I met Nora and the two boys as well – your grandmother occasionally had them round for dinner.

'It must have been after about a year that I noticed that there were problems between your father and Nora. As I've said, your father, throughout his life, never took his responsibilities seriously. He was a romantic, a gambler, a frustrated poet who could never quite reconcile himself to life as a family doctor. He was still living at Tahir's with his family, even though he must have been earning good money as a doctor. Nora understandably wanted them to have a house of their own, no woman likes to be beholden to the charity of others, and when your father prevaricated once too often she moved into a hotel, taking the two boys with her. Goodness knows why your father hadn't troubled to find a home for his family; perhaps he was broke and was too afraid to tell her. Anyway, after a couple of days in the hotel she and the boys boarded a ship back to England without so much as a word to your father. I suppose you couldn't blame her, really. I saw enough of your father's fickleness over the years to understand exactly what she must have gone through.

'It was Tahir who found out about it. He must have seen them at the docks. He telephoned your father immediately, but by the time he got there the ship had already left. He followed them, taking the next available sailing. When he returned to Karachi, however, it was without his family. I don't recall the details, but it seemed that their marriage was over. Janny did eventually follow him here, your father had managed to get him an introduction with PIA to train as a pilot, but Nora and Yusuf remained in England. It was around that time that I got to know your father well and he eventually proposed marriage to me. I refused at first; I wasn't happy about the fact that he was already married. But he persisted, telling me that his wife was a Catholic and couldn't divorce. He was a Muslim himself, of course, and so it was quite legitimate for him to take a second wife, but it wasn't until Janny gave his agreement too that I felt that I was able to accept the proposal.'

I didn't understand everything that my mother was telling me; I still wanted to know why Janny never played with me if he was my brother. But I was still intrigued by the lady in the photograph.

'Where's Nora now?' I asked.

'She died, Zeeba. She died a long time ago. I remember that your father was devastated when he heard, and took the first plane back to England to be with Yusuf. You see, he never forgot Nora. He couldn't live with her, but he couldn't forget her.'

My mother paused, perhaps remembering her own grief now. She stood up from the seat, walked over to the open drawer of the desk, and picked up the other two photographs. Sitting down again she picked up Nora's picture and fanned the three out together, holding them up for me to see.

'Your father's families,' she smiled proudly. 'They were always with him here in the surgery.' She stroked my hair as I stared at the photographs. 'Nora, Jan, Yusuf, Zeeba, and me,' she went on. 'Dr Sadiq, his wives, and his children.'